GLOUCESTERSHIRE

Edited by Allison Dowse

First published in Great Britain in 2000 by
YOUNG WRITERS
Remus House,
Coltsfoot Drive,
Peterborough, PE2 9JX
Telephone (01733) 890066

HB ISBN 0 75432 282 3
SB ISBN 0 75432 283 1

FOREWORD

This year, the Young Writers' Up, Up & Away competition proudly presents a showcase of the best poetic talent from over 70,000 up-and-coming writers nationwide.

Successful in continuing our aim of promoting writing and creativity in children, our regional anthologies give a vivid insight into the thoughts, emotions and experiences of today's younger generation, displaying their inventive writing in its originality.

The thought, effort, imagination and hard work put into each poem impressed us all and again the task of editing proved challenging due to the quality of entries received, but was nevertheless enjoyable. We hope you are as pleased as we are with the final selection and that you continue to enjoy *Up, Up & Away Gloucestershire* for many years to come.

CONTENTS

Sam Vijay	70
Michael Blackford	70
Katrina Locke	71
Sharlette Johnson	71
Natasha Ogden	72
Natalya Gale	72
James Carpenter	73
Abigail Locke	73
Ricky Breach	74
Anouska Callander	74
Sheniece Brown	75
Kevin Cox	75
Kimberley Woods	75
Victoria Scott	76
Gareth Peers	76
Aaron Singh	77
Jacqueline Jacobs	77
Owen Higgins	78
Karl Holland	78
Natasha Phillips	78
Josh Merrett	79
Joseph Critchley	80
Karina Clutterbuck	80
Paige Satherley	80
Daniel Walker	81
Jennifer Heath	82
Danielle Gordon-Waugh	82
Daniel Vijay	82
Collette Peers	83
Anne Carpenter	83
Rebecca Allen	84
Robert Folley	84
Emma Willetts	84
Aaron Lee	85

North Cerney CE School

Michael Rogers	86
Jamie Salazar	87
Kelly Moy	87
Huw Rettie	88
Robet Gardiner	88
William Seymour & Ben Barton	89

Northleach CE Primary School

Daniel Hilder	89
Fay Davies	90
Thomas See	90
Jessica Wills	91
Dominic Higgs	91
Adam Hubbard	91
Kim Welch	92
Luke Dooner	92
James Binns	93
Jonathan Salmon	93
George Chilton	94
Dean Wharton	94
Jordan Miller	95

Noreton CE Primary School

Emily Meadows	95
Charlotte Pritchard	96
Michelle Keel-Stocker	96
Claire Overal	97
Simon Curtis	97
Sophie Brammer	98
Zeb D-Matty	98
Jonathan Biruls	99
Amy Davis	99
Emilie Dill	100
Jack Lewis	101
Katie Fox	102

Tuffley Primary School

The Poems

SUMMER SEASIDE

You can go to the
Seaside in summer.
You can watch the
Seagulls fly.
You can swim in the
Deep blue water
And eat ice-cream,
While you dry.

You can go to the
Seaside in summer,
Have a picnic
By the sea,
With lemonade and buns,
Make sandcastles,
By the sea,
And decorate with
Stones and shells.
And when the tide comes in
You go home.

And you're happy
Because of a day
Beside the sea.

Emily Lomax (9)

RAIN

Pouring down, slashing around,
As cars go by on the ground
Slish slosh, pish posh.

Children playing in the rain
They come back, watching the rain
Wondering if it will be good like pie,
Or bad, please not or I will cry.

Rain, rain, rain, I hate the rain I do, I do, I do!
People wearing plastic hats how horrid!
'Specially in the splashing rain.

Running around in the pouring rain
Pish posh, slish slosh.

Splashing in the puddles getting feet wet,
How horrid, I'd rather be
Home in my bed.

Sureyya Pethania (10)
Airthrie School

WORMS

Squiggling wriggling
Through the soil.
A little worm is on his way.
He slithers along
The damp grass
To a pile of leaves.
Munch, munch
He eats the leaves
Helping the garden grow.

Jonathan Bradbeer (10)
Airthrie School

THE STORM

Woke up early,
Rain was beating on my window
Haven't slept all night,
Lightning flashed and thunder crashed
Got dressed,
Lots of layers to keep me warm
Ate my breakfast,
Hot toast and warm coffee
Got in the car to go to school,
Windscreen wipers squeaking
Got out of the car,
Ran to school hood up
Maths first, couldn't think
No play, too wet
English now,
Wrote only a few sentences
Lunch now,
Wasn't hungry
No play again,
Still too wet
Art next,
Did a picture of a storm
Went home,
Rushed homework,
Wasn't thinking
Watched television,
In front of a fire
Went to bed, really early.

Vicky Livingstone Thompson (9)
Airthrie School

THE SEAGULL

Soaring, gliding, wheeling,
Floating, diving, squealing,
Yellow beaked,
Black eyed,
Flying silhouette against a blue sky.

Diving for salmon,
With sharp talons,
And wings tipped with grey,
Through the wind,
Through the storm,
Any weather,
Doesn't matter.

Flying, flitting, hovering, dipping
For his family's living,
For the children's life,
Industrious, unselfish,
An example for us all,
Soaring over a blue sea.

Charlotte Roberts (9)
Airthrie School

BILL

My dad Bill
Lives in a mill
That lives on a hill

He has a job
And his partner is called Bob
And he likes corn on the cob

He is always late
But he has a good mate
His dinner waits on his plate

Our last holiday was in Spain
We had to leave, Bill had a pain
Now he has gone completely insane.

Hannah Ford (10)
Airthrie School

NETBALL

I was chosen for the netball team
That Wednesday
I stepped onto the court
I started to get butterflies

I looked at our opponents
They were twice as tall as me
I sunk into my skin

We started to play
A strange loud voice shouted off-side

We started, I got the ball
It went to Katie, to me
I had a chance at shooting

The ball was going in, in, in
Whoo it went in
I started jumping up and down
The match was over
The score eleven nil to *us!*

Sophie Wilding (10)
Airthrie School

CREEPY CRAWLIES

Spiders crawling up your back all night
Wake up in the morning they'll give you a fright
Scattering around your bedroom all day
Only wanting for a play
Making webs with a sticky wet glue
Somewhere to sleep like me or you

Wasps and flies flying around
Stings and itches without any sound
Trying to catch them it's simply no use
For prancing and dancing helps your energy too

Cockroaches come with a clack clack clack
You'll find them in your hat hat hat

Ants making nests under your bed
Once they've got out of the farm
You made the other day

All in all they are horrible things
Creeping around your room
Doing what they shouldn't be.

Georgia Hughes (9)
Airthrie School

CANDLELIGHT

Think of candles big and small,
Used most of the time when lights stall,
There's nothing better than to relax,
To smell the flames and burning wax.

Feel the heat on your face,
The candle needs some space,
All the colours of burning light,
Glowing safely in the night.

Christopher Quiney (9)
Airthrie School

CANDLE

In the dark
I see a flame
Dancing in the light
On its own.

I fell to the ground
I hear it whisper
In the night.

I thought it was my mum
I tried to shout
It wouldn't come out.

I got up, I see another light,
I close my eyes
The lights are on again.

It was a dream
I told myself,
But when I go downstairs
I know that a candle
Is as special as a dream.

Natalie Skulskyj (10)
Airthrie School

CANDLELIGHT

Once I lit a candle
A very little candle
And while I looked at it
A lot of thoughts came to me.
Peace
Fire
Relax
Teddy bears
Jesus
Bed
Church.
Relax. Relax.

And while I watched it burning,
I smelt the lovely scent.
It reminded me of grandparents
Long since gone;
And of Jesus:
Who is the brightest light.

Peter Denley (9)
Airthrie School

CANDLELIGHT

I lit a candle one day.
It reminded me of the sweet scent of a flower
Shining in the sun's rays.
The candle was burning like a tiny flame of fire.
It feels like that candle has real magic powers.

Its soft and peaceful scent is burning everywhere.
Its gleam shines in my hair.
The flame is glowing like a golden silk mat.
I love the scent of the melted wax
As I sit in my chair and relax.

Panisha Patel (9)
Airthrie School

CANDLE

When I light a
candle one night
I thought
warmth
peace
quiet
and
love
Most of all
my grandad
who died when
I was six.
The candle died
away so I have to
wait for another day
to light my candle
again.

Emma Lavery (10)
Airthrie School

THE FOX

The thunder of hooves
The cry of the horn
        Lives for pleasure
        Is it really worth it?
Round the bend
Dogs baying at his feet
        Lives for pleasure
        Is it really worth it?
The crack of the pistol
Grass spraying up around
        Lives for pleasure
        Is it really worth it?
In his den
He'll be safe there
        Lives for pleasure
        Is it really worth it?
Dogs at the front
Out the back
        Lives for pleasure
        Is it really worth it?
The crack of a pistol
He falls down dead
        Lives for pleasure
        Is it really worth it?
Hung up for display
On the road to extinction
        Lives for pleasure
        Is it really worth it?

Kit Heawood (9)
Airthrie School

CANDLELIGHT

Candlelight,
Candle bright,
Wizardry, dragon fight.
Silver, gold,
Gallant, bold
Dripping wax,
Burning flax
Peace, love
Stars above.
New, old
Stories told.

Candlelight
Candle bright.

Amber Cross (9)
Airthrie School

CANDLES

Candle light, candle bright
The excitement I see tonight,
Burning away,
Like a tower made of gold.
By the light of a candle,
Stories can be told -
Peace and quiet
Everybody will enjoy it!
The smells of burning candles -
The best thing that can be lit.

Rose Clarke (9)
Airthrie School

A CANDLE POEM

Think of peace,
Think of harmony,
Think of people,
From the past,
Smell the burning,
Far away,
Makes you feel
Good and gay,
See the colours
Orange and blue,
Think of other
People as well
As you.

Miles Beardsley (9)
Airthrie School

CANDLELIGHT

I think of soft thoughts,
Fluffy thoughts,
Peace, relax,
I think of old days,
Victorians,
Cold days,
Tranquillity, love,
Straining eyes,
Aching thighs,
Dripping wax,
Just relax,
Think of good times and rhymes.

Philip Ellis (10)
Airthrie School

CANDLES

Candles make me think of home,
At my home it is nice and warm,
I miss it so much,
I wish I could go home.

Candles make me peaceful,
Don't rush around, settle down,
Listen to carol singers,
Go home and think about candles.

Rebecca Cotterill (9)
Airthrie School

MY FAMILY

My dad likes watching football,
Live or on the telly at home.
And if he is not doing that,
He's in the bath eating foam!

My mum likes going shopping,
And eating fish for tea.
And when she catches them from the coast,
She insists on taking me!

My brother likes playing with his friend,
And going to his house.
And when he goes there every day,
He pretends to be a mouse!

Sophie Thomas (11)
Calton Junior School

FUNKY GIRL

A colourful, bright, wacky girl,
Round head, big smile.
Orange hair, shocking hat,
Crop top with pink spots.
Flared trousers, colourful stripes,
Platform shoes, sunny yellow.

Blue eyes, long lashes,
Peach skin, red lips.
Purple nails, very long,
Green toenails, very short.
Really cool, very pretty,
You know her name, it's
Funky girl!

Justine Freeman (11)
Calton Junior School

WHY?

Why is a poet, a poet?
Why is a cat, a cat?
Why do we live?
Why do we die?
Why am I young?
Why are people old?
Why do we shrivel up?
Why do we go bald?
Why do we go home?
Why, why, why, tell me why?
                    Because . . .

Cassie Lewis (11)
Calton Junior School

HEDGEHOG

I once had a hedgehog called Queer,
Who always seemed to drink beer.
One day he went pink,
And fell down the sink
And that was the end of Queer.

Alice White (11)
Calton Junior School

BIRTHDAY

Presents for me
party food on the table
party games are waiting for me
good food.

Jolene Carpenter (10)
Calton Junior School

RUGBY

People running from side to side
Sprinting round like mad
But please don't drop the ball,
Because if you do it, you are very bad.

Daniel Portlock (10)
Calton Junior School

DOGS AND CATS!

D is for Dalmatians,
O is for old sheep dogs,
G is for German Shepherds,
S is for sheep dogs.

A is for animals,
N is for nature,
D is for daisies.

C is for Cornish rex cats,
A is for American shorthair cats,
T is for Turkish van cats,
S is for sphinx cats.

Tara Hennessy (11)
Calton Junior School

DANGER

My mum says 'It's dangerous to talk to strangers,
They might take you away.'

My dad says 'It's dangerous to jump on the stairs,
It's safer to go out to play!'

My sister says 'Don't play with strange cats,
They can bite very hard and scratch.'

My brother says 'Don't swim in deep sea,
Although swimming pools are not a patch.'

But I say 'Danger doesn't bother me,
Just have fun - why can't they see?'

Olivia Jeffree (11)
Calton Junior School

Epitaph On Unfortunate Persons

Here lies old colour-blind Jed,
Thought the traffic lights were green
But they were actually red.

There is a young man who's a scouse
Who makes fireworks in his house,
'Til he dropped his cigar
In the gunpowder jar
Well there *was* a young man in a house!

The man that lies beneath here
Was trodden on by a deer.
The deer went mad
'Cos his food went bad
That's the story of him beneath 'ere.

Tom Cassidy (10)
Calton Junior School

A Dolphin's Life

D olphins swimming day and night
O tters have a try
L ovely whales join the fun
P ractice and you'll be just like them
H erring is always eating the fish
I t's lovely down at the sea today
N oises are low they never rise
S o swim there forever.
        A dolphin's life is fantastic.

Jade Pulley (11)
Calton Junior School

CRAZY

Groovy
Silly
Don't forget
Mad
Stupid
Crazy
People are
Sad.

Elaine Phelpstead (10)
Calton Junior School

SUMMER

S   ummer is hot,
U   mberellas up and down,
M   e and my friends are playing around,
M   um and Dad sunbathing all day,
E   arly in the morning the day is dawning,
R   omance is in the air as the light is falling.

Rachael Burnham (11)
Calton Junior School

LISTEN . . .

To the sound of
wrapping paper scrunching
smiling faces all around me
Happy.

Fay Bizsley (10)
Calton Junior School

WHAT YOU CAN DO WITH A RULER

You can
Snap it or paint it
And fasten it in the table
You can draw on it and
Hurl it at the wall! Bend it
Sit on it and lock it under your chair
Or maybe if you want to
You can twist it in your hair
You can chew it you can lick it
You can drop it on the floor
You can saw the table as well
Or maybe even stick it in your shoe!
You can open up your book with it
And use it as a bookmark and maybe
If you really want you can use it
As a catapult too,
Flick
Your
Rubber about! Or play swords too!

Tom Imeson (8)
Charlton Kings Junior School

ELECTRIC THING

Its long spiky tail
And every tiny arms
Electric shocks powerful
Enough to paralyse anything
Its cheeks bright yellow
And as round as a ball
And once he's shocked you
You'll fall off the wall!

Jack Gardner (9)
Charlton Kings Junior School

BLODIN

Burn village to ash
like smallest mouse . . .
Mighty huge shadow
Sky scraper,
Teeth pointed sharp swords,
With an exploding volcano
Claws sharp daggers.

Hide carved of
smooth,
           solid
metal,
whirlwind.
with no whirl
           slowly stomps.

He is what orders the world around.

Named
           Blodin!

Born a *beast!*

Rhiannon V Sheridan (8)
Charlton Kings Junior School

MY MAGIC BOX POEM

I will put in my box
The last snowflake on a snowy night
And a flicker of a peaceful rainbow.

I will put in my box
The last sip from the calmest sea
And a last sight of a turtle.

I will put in my box
The last spark from a silver dolphin.

My box is fashioned with the sparkle of the sea
With clear water in the corners
And stars on the lid.

Kirsty Bee (8)
Charlton Kings Junior School

MY RULER

Bend the ruler backwards, split it at the end
Praise it, praise it, praise it, it's a godsend

Bang it on the table, throw it in the air
Stuff up your jumper
Hide it in an eclair

Throw it at the teacher
She'll say 'Don't you dare'

Put it in your custard
Dip it in your mustard

Throw it at your horse
(You'll die of course)
Make it vibrate quickly
Shred the paper to tears
Tears of papers all of mine
So it always gets the stares.

Guy Lusty (9)
Charlton Kings Junior School

BLODIN

I'm ugly, filthy, grubby and lazy,
I'm ghostly and . . .
Downright stupid

I have sharp pointed teeth
I snore in my sleep, I live down in the deep
I'm a beastly beast

I scatter above you . . .
Watching you
Peering through the branches

The slaves toil nervously
I hover
I hover
I hover
I hover
I disappear
through
the
mountains.

Jemma Louise Lusty (7)
Charlton Kings Junior School

THE WINTER WIND

The winter wind is
damp and icy,
the autumn wind is playful
The summer wind is warm and sweet,
and floats gently through the air.

The wind I love the best,
comes freezing after dawn,
feeling cool and calm against my face,
sweeping, swirling round my feet,
the wind after dawn.

Vanessa Burton (9)
Charlton Kings Junior School

ROLLER-COASTER

Once I went on a roller-coaster
get in the seat get strapped
and 3 2 1
we were going as
fast as light
up and down
twirling, swirling
the person I was sitting next to
was sick
and then
down, down
down
until
I
reach
the
ground.

Phoebe Johnston (9)
Charlton Kings Junior School

DINOSAURS

Dinosaurs are big and strong
With everlasting life
They feed on leaves
And stroll around at night
With big long claws and gaping jaws
I chase and catch my prey
I bite
I claw
And tear them limb from limb
I roar aloud
And charge and growl
Dying down, down, down and down.

Joseph Perry (8)
Charlton Kings Junior School

BLODIN

Cones on my teeth,
brave and ferocious,
as fierce as a snake,
drink oil,
love oil,
thump loudly,
scatter through village,
whizzes like a maze,
covered with black coal
I'm called . . . *Blodin.*

Anna Hayward (7)
Charlton Kings Junior School

BLODIN THE BEAST

When asleep sun shines perfectly,
When awake sky is sombre.
Bloooodin
Massive, monster, oil slurper,
Overweight, stout, monstrous monster.
Blooodin
Forces the world around,
Stalks over mountains.
Bloooodin
Last Blodin
To ever live.
Bloooodin
When villagers encounter
him they exclaim
Blodin
Blodin
Blodin
Blodin
Oh gosh I'm dead!

Nicole Edwards (8)
Charlton Kings Junior School

WHAT AM I?

I am an orange winged giant,
Spitfire, furnace always triumphs,
A very tough battler as you think,
Because spitfire kills and kills,
A very tough battler each other say,
As you lead yourself into dismay.

Fire-breath dragon.

Joe Barton (8)
Charlton Kings Junior School

BLODIN

Like a dragon breathing out
Blazing fire.
Drinks oil roars like a dinosaur
The world trembles when he stamps
Like an elephant
Terrifies the village slaves.
He is *ginormous*
Lazy
Sculpted a murky world for
Village slaves,
Is made out of stones,
They rattled down from his body lumber
About like a lazy person
Who thinks he rules the world
Who thinks he is king when
He gets up he mumbles and
Mutters good inside bad outside
Sabretooth teeth. Black as ebony.
People look like tiny ants to him
But to the people he is a
                    Giant.

Nicola Lawrance (7)
Charlton Kings Junior School

ANIMALS

Lots of them
all over the world
tigers, lions, leopards,
monkeys.

Animals there
are all different ones
dark, spotty, dotted,
striped, but the best one
is a *lion.*

Kirsty Griffin (8)
Charlton Kings Junior School

BLODIN THE BEAST

World wobbles like a quivering
Jelly on a plate.
Black clouds surround the planet Earth.
Houses fall down like magic.
Teeth as sharp as a unicorn's horn
Or
Maybe they're as sharp as rusty nails,
I won't tell you, you'll soon find out!
Grrrr!
Here he comes!
Heart beating fast, quicker than a blast
Of a rocket zooming into space.
Breathes burning hot fire, drinks smoky black
Scalier than a crocodile back. Skin detail is just like
a tree stump.
Bigger than an icy, snowy mountain that almost touches the sky.
The scary, scaly, frightful, huge, ugly, wicked, terrifying . . .
Hang on, who am I talking about here?

Blodin!

Laura Webb (8)
Charlton Kings Junior School

WHAT AM I?

I swirl
I swoop
I'm the colour of a pearl

I fly
I screech
I cry out loud by the sea

I rule the skies
And all that flies
Until I'm the one that dies
What am I?

Rosy Jones (9)
Charlton Kings Junior School

BLODIN THE BEAST!

Essssstimate . . .
Who I am.
Large and monstrous.
Stalking through the mountains,
Slumbering like a hill.
My fire - like a setting sun
In the middle of summer.
Blodin.

Alexandra Andow (7)
Charlton Kings Junior School

BLODIN THE BEAST

The only dinosaur that is
not extinct
droops around the ashes
His eyes red in rage
The monster opens his
hideous mouth and reveals
his sword-like teeth
oil gobbler
ground shaker
bone cruncher.

Harry Mowat Maconochie (7)
Charlton Kings Junior School

BLODIN

Destroys villages
Scorches people to death
Strides over villages
Breathes fire
Faster than a rocket
Stomps around villages
Wrecks buildings
Houses
Hotels
Black ugly heart.

Markos Ataou (7)
Charlton Kings Junior School

BLODIN

Who am I?
Iron-like?
Who blazes villages to shreds,
As black as pitch black?
Who's as hideous as a pig?
As beastly as a sombre rain cloud,
Who's meanest brute in the world?
Whose ugly heart is inky,
As ginormous as a skyscraper?
The only dinosaur that exists,
Who loves oil?
Blodin the beast.

John Trevaskis (7)
Charlton Kings Junior School

BLODIN THE BEAST

Thundering towards Hosea came the one and only monster Blodin.
Razor sharp teeth as sharp as a knife
Blodin the extensive monster still stamping towards Hosea.
He's crossing the river with the monster behind
And in goes Blodin and that's the end of that monster.

Jacob Salter (7)
Charlton Kings Junior School

A MISERABLE DAY

Click-clack, click-clack; hypnotised
The machines ringing in my head.
Miserably plodding home.
Hunger strikes, my stomach grumbles like an awakening volcano.
The evening sky like a dragon's breath.
Huge buildings towering over me like a vast blanket.
I'm in complete darkness.
Trudging along not thinking,
The way home is always the same,
Automatically, I turn the corners
Then I see the only tree in the whole street,
A tall oak tree standing shock still outside my house,
I smile.
I'm happy to be home again.

Tamsin Keeling (10)
Clearwell CE Primary School

A LONG DAY AT WORK

Busy, busy, busy all around me
Weary, worn out and exhausted.
Marching homewards like a swarm of ants,
Head down, bent down,
Every day the same.
The city is a maze of buildings.
The towers poise over me,
Like hungry tigers watching their prey.
A smile grows on my face as I reach home.

Hester Cross
Clearwell CE Primary School

COMING HOME FROM WORK

I feel exhausted as if I've been in a chase.
I can hear the clang, clang, clang
It's like I am in a bad dream and I can't get out.
My headache is getting worse and worse
When at last the bell rings
I get in the queue scrambling to get outside.
I feel the breeze stroke my hair as it flies past
I walk along the never-ending, winding road.
The towering buildings look down at me as I stroll home.
At last I turn the final corner.
I see my children waiting to greet me.
Home at last.

Gregory Cantrill (11)
Clearwell CE Primary School

GOING TO WORK

Trudging down the street,
Another boring day at work.
Listening to the growling of the machines
I walk through the gates.
Now starts the blood-trembling noise.
All day making bread.
Dust everywhere.
Home is on my mind.
Got to get out of here.
But still more work.

Annie Rose Spayne (10)
Clearwell CE Primary School

COMING FROM THE MILL

Click clack click clack.
I can't wait to get back,
Rushing from the mill,
Running down the hill,
Click clack click clack.

Clip clop clip clop,
I can't stop,
I can't wait to go home
Where I'm all alone,
Clip clop clip clop.

Munch munch munch munch,
At last my lunch.
Then I go to bed
Yawn! I rest my head.
Munch munch munch munch.

Lucy Parker (9)
Clearwell CE Primary School

THE MILL

Clickety clack, clickety clack
Dusty, dusty it's so dusty.
The old machines are so, so rusty
The noise is in my head.
Oh I am thinking about my bed.
I am so hungry.
I am hypnotised by the wheel going round.
I hate this sound.
I hear the bell, we all go out.
We are so happy we all shout.

Laura Jane Pryce (10)
Clearwell CE Primary School

GOING TO WORK

Afraid am I,
When the factory is in my eye.
I wish I could be late
So I wouldn't hear the sound
Of the blaring machines.
Clitter, clatter, clitter clatter.
Bouncing round in my head.
Surrounding me all day long.
Clitter, clatter, clitter, clatter
Finally the bell screams,
I am exhausted.
I'm glad to go home,
To my wife and my children.

Darren Parker (10)
Clearwell CE Primary School

COMING HOME FROM WORK

Chattering and shuffling,
Crowding all around me,
I glance up at the evening sky.
The buildings towering over me.
Exhausted, I turn a corner,
More factories, more people
Darkness closing in on me.
The smoky streets of Salford narrow,
My children greet me.

Michaela Wall (10)
Clearwell CE Primary School

COMING HOME FROM WORK

Click, clack, clack and click go the machines at the mill.
Finally the bell goes and it's the end of the day.
I join the teaming crowds going towards the door like a pack of dogs.
I get out into the foggy, smelly, dark lane.
I trudge gloomily past some children with hoops and balls.
I hope when I get in dinner will be on the table.
Coming home from work tired, exhausted
But looking forward to see my children.
At last my house is in sight
I'm home warm, content and away from the blaring machines.

Tom Jackson (10)
Clearwell CE Primary School

END OF WORK

The tallness of the chimneys
The darkness of the smoke
The noises of the factory
The sadness of the folk
The towering buildings black from smoke
The screaming of the children coming home from school
The houses full of people with no money
Like mine, number *ten.*
All the things I've seen
I will see again.

Danny John Williams (9)
Clearwell CE Primary School

COMING FROM THE MILL

Click, clack, click, clack,
I'm coming from the mill.
Going past the towering buildings,
Here I go her I go.
I can't wait to get home,
To see what's for tea.
Trudging, plodding, trudging, plodding
The mill is behind me.
When I get home, I see my lovely wife.
Click, clack, click, clack,
I'm coming from the mill.

Toni Hopkinson (10)
Clearwell CE Primary School

CATS

Cats are scratchy and patchy,
Cats are tatty and chatty.
Cats sleep on a mat,
Cats curl up on your lap.
Cats might bite,
Cats might fight,
Cats go out at night.

Rosie Kemp (5)
Clearwell CE Primary School

TIGER

Tiger orange and black
Tiger big and soft
Tiger fierce and scary
Tiger stays so still
Tiger runs so far
Tiger clever and fast
Tiger pounce and kill.

Lewis Morgan-Brain (6)
Clearwell CE Primary School

CATS

Cats are sleepy,
Cats are patchy.
Cats are ginger,
Cats are white.
Cats smell fishy,
Cats are nasty,
Cats are warm,
Cats bite.

Amie Lloyd (7)
Clearwell CE Primary School

TIGER

Tiger run
Tiger yellow
Tiger orange and black
Tiger roar
Tiger hunt
Tiger stripy back.

Bradley Jones (5)
Clearwell CE Primary School

TIGER

Tiger furry and stripy,
Tiger orange and black.
Tiger bite and fight,
Tiger pounce and kill.
Tiger play and hunt,
Tiger scary and roar.
Tiger sharp teeth and sharp claws,
Tiger fierce and still.

Lianne Osley (6)
Clearwell CE Primary School

TIGER

Tiger orange and black
Tiger soft and furry
Tiger sharp teeth and claws
Tiger play and fight
Tiger hunt and run
Tiger bite and creep
Tiger pounce and kill
Tiger fierce and roar.

George Rogers (6)
Clearwell CE Primary School

TIGER

Tiger orange and black,
Tiger yellow and stripy.
Tiger sharp claws and teeth,
Tiger furry and soft.
Tiger hunt and roar,
Tiger run and kill,
Tiger pounce and creep,
Tiger fight and bite.

Tanya Alexander (7)
Clearwell CE Primary School

THE THING

As I walk into the cold bleak mist,
I hear the rushing waterfall,
Suddenly something catches my eye,
A black shadow. What could it be?
As it gets closer it starts to emerge,
I'm so scared, I can hear its heart beating,
I try to run but it runs too fast,
Then I'm just about to go over the fence,
As it jumps onto its hind legs,
My head turns as it comes down with a crash,
The ground shakes, as dust comes out of the ground,
It comes extremely close,
I can see its eyes glaring at me,
As I can hear and feel its breath,
I touch its silky black hairs
I still don't know what it is,
I walk into the mud and go around the side,
It's twice my size and even more and I find out it's a stallion.

Emma Bennett (10)
Frenchay CE Primary School

THE CRASHING RAIN

The rain comes crashing down
From the dark gloomy sky
With its blue overcoat,
It darkens the land.
The clouds are as grey as a
Pigeon's feather.

The water creates a swimming pool
For all the ducks and geese that live nearby.
The rain smashes down
With his gun at the ready
To shoot anyone who is outside.
The people ogle out of the window.
The rain makes big puddles that
Get bigger and bigger.
Suddenly the rain goes soft and
Starts spitting and then it slowly stops.
All the people look out of their windows
With astonishment.

Kieran Phillips (10)
Frenchay CE Primary School

THE STORM HORSE

As I snuggled under my covers,
The storm clouds rolled in and darkened the sky,
From his icy lair the storm horse came,
With flaming eyes the colour of the sun,
Which burnt the landscape with his lightning stare.

His ferocious nostrils sending out huge clouds of steam,
As he thunders over his dark rain clouds,
He drums his hooves on the great concrete earth,
As his tears thunder down.

Suddenly Dawn the lion steps out from his sun palace.
With a mighty roar that shook the whole world,
Dawn charges at the storm horse,
With a terrified neigh the storm horse retreats,
As the proud lion returns to his morning home.

Megan Woolcock (11)
Frenchay CE Primary School

THE MOMENT OF TRUTH

The match has started
The ball has been kicked
The first thing I see is the ball coming towards me
What shall I do?
My heart is pumping
Pump, pump, pump
I know what I will do
Dribble, dribble, dribble
Someone from the other team is coming
So tackle, tackle, tackle
Success so carry on
Dribble, dribble, dribble
The goal is getting closer and closer
And shoot
The goal keeper dives into the air
This is the moment of truth
A *star* is born.

Omar Sherif (11)
Frenchay CE Primary School

DYNAMIC DANCING DOLPHIN

I watch my magnificently breath-taking dolphin,
Graciously moving,
Jumping high, touching the bright blue sky.
A splosh, so towering, it turns into
Glorious, whispy bubbles,
The adventurous dolphin flips and flops
Through the rippling waves.
Its eyes twinkling in the shining sun,
Having so much enjoyable fun.
A face as smooth as a baby's skin,
Nose shiny, sleek and soft.
Its slender body, dazzling, diving,
Through the everlasting sea,
My dolphin whistles to me.
I love you darling dolphin.

Lizzie Aldous (10)
Frenchay CE Primary School

GOLDFISH

A beautiful gold pretty creature
Swimming around your bright blue tank.
Its luscious silver tail cracks the surface.
It whizzes through the wound up weeds.
Pushes its head through the multi-coloured pebbles.
It goes in every crack and corner in the crumbling castle.
He loves to play with the micro fish right at the top of the tank.
He is my goldfish, my crazy gold friend,
Right in the centre of his magical water home.

Huw Rees (10)
Frenchay CE Primary School

GORILLA!

Gorilla, gorilla, looking at me,
What do you see, gorilla? What do you see?
Guess what I see, I see you!
Big and hairy, (sorry, it's true)

Hairy, rough, huge, fat,
Gorilla, you look worse than my fat cat!
'Aarrrggghhh!' says gorilla,
'Grrr' goes me,
'I don't like you, gorilla, you scare me.'

'Aaarrrggghhh,' once again roars the gorilla,
'Arggh' goes me,
Teacher! Teacher! Help me! Help me!
'The gorilla's after me.'

Crashing through the city,
Running through the town,
Gorillas everywhere!
Lopping houses down.
Crash!

Sweaty, wet, hot and sat up in my bed,
I realise it's just a dream,
Just a dream,
Just a dream,
Just a dream,
Just a . . . *zzzz! zzzz!*

Darrelle Jolley (11)
Frenchay CE Primary School

HAMSTER HUDDLE

As she comes out her little house
Her bright pink nose sniffs the air,
She stretches out as quiet as a mouse
Then she does a pose like a teddy bear.

She creeps into her exercise wheel
Running round so fast,
Then she stops to have a delicious meal
After that she jumps and climbs like a gymnast.

She bites the bars and wants to come out
I take her into her ball,
Then she runs and scurries about
Afterwards I hold her tightly so she doesn't fall.

Her golden brown fur blows in the light
I put her back in her house,
Now it's time to say goodnight
She hops back in as quiet as a mouse.

Rachel Withers (9)
Frenchay CE Primary School

MY CAT

My cat gazes at me with its curious, staring eyes,
She curls up on my comfy lap,
I stroke her silky, soft and smooth dark cloak,
It droops over her velvet skin,
She laps up her creamy milk
And gobbles up her juicy meat,
At the end of the day
She purrs about a dream of her luxurious day,
Prrrrrrrr!

Sophie Kear (10)
Frenchay CE Primary School

THE MEAN DOG!

There's a dog from the woods
That is handsome and smart
He is wild he is grey
He growls and he barks.

He is smooth he is clean
He is silky and soft
He is lean he is mean
He is wild and likes to catch moths.

He howls at the moon so big and round
And bays it all the time when lying on the ground.
He creeps and he scratches
He's alert all the time
he yelps and he yowls
And snatches every time.

He's a mongrel and he's mad
And he's very cute and sweet
But when you come close to him
He may bite your feet.

He whines and he whimpers
He snarls and snaps
He quarrels and scampers
And he leaps on people's backs.

Adrian Reed (10)
Frenchay CE Primary School

My Friend's Dog Beppie

(Especially for Freya Grace Collins)

Beppie is a wonderful dog
Beppie is my friend
Beppie is the sweetest dog
Who drives you round the bend

His fur is as white as snow
His bark is as sweet as a nut
He is just so small and cuddly
He would fit in a rabbit's hut

His paws are as small as chestnuts
He's playful and he's fun
He's just so sweet
He really is
He's my little currant bun

Beppie is a wonderful dog
Beppie is my friend
Beppie is the sweetest dog
Who drives you round the bend.

Jade Standish (10)
Frenchay CE Primary School

Cat

Cat, cat, beautiful cat.
Your soft silky fur runs through my fingers like milk,
Yes, like milk.

Cat, cat, dazzling cat.
Your black ears are soft as water dripping on my fingers.
Your black nose warms me up
As I sit by the roaring fire.

Cat, cat, beautiful cat.
You know I love you, don't you. 'Are you sure?'
Yes, I'm sure and you'll always be my cat.
My cat, my cat.

Emma Bye (10)
Frenchay CE Primary School

THE OTTER

The otter swims gracefully through the crystal water,
like a dolphin swimming towards its destiny.
Its fur shines in the sun like the morning's dew.
It dashes into a log like a fish trying
to get away from a hungry shark.
The otter's eyes sparkle like a diamond ring.
It catches a fish like a bear fishing for salmon,
then it goes into its hole to have a nice sleep.

Laura Deytrikh (9)
Frenchay CE Primary School

DOLPHIN

Dolphins are such pretty creatures
They have all different kinds of features
They swim freely through the ocean curling
and swirling all of their body in motion
They are so pretty like they use potion
to make them look beautiful.

Abigail Long (9)
Frenchay CE Primary School

HAMSTERS

Sniffing around, always hungry for food,
Their tiny paws make a crunching noise on the sawdust.
The lively fluff ball scatters up and down its cage,
Now I can hear the rumbling of its wheel,
Spinning round faster than lightning striking.
It feels warm as I first get it out of its cage,
I manage to stroke the jumpy thing,
But oh no, it's climbing up to my shoulder,
And takes a brave jump back to my cold hands,
I safely put the hamster back in her paradise cage.

Rebecca Leek (11)
Frenchay CE Primary School

MILLENNIUM BUGS

M illennium Bugs look odd,
I think they smell of cod,
L ook around, can you see?
L ippy they can be.
E nd the fun, will they come?
N aughty bugs love to hum.
N ow it is time to solve the mystery
I think it would help to use history.
U nderneath their shell
M illennium Bugs love to yell.
B ugging Bugs hang about
U nderneath, you know they're out.
G urgle down the plughole,
S lug-like creatures the colour of coal.

Alys Fletcher (10)
Frenchay CE Primary School

Puppy Dogs!

P uppies, puppies are so sweet.
U nhappy puppies because they've done something wrong.
P layful puppies get worn out.
P roud parents of the dog when he's done something good.
Y ou think they won't grow big.

D ogs are cute and friendly,
O nly some are fierce,
G rowling at the pussycat,
S narling at each other.

Jennie Brown (10)
Frenchay CE Primary School

Sunset

The howling of the wind
And the crashing of sea
On the jagged rocks.
The golden sand glistening
In the sunset.
A man on the end of the pier
As he casts his rod out
Into the shadows of the sea.
As I look, the clouds
Look as if they are a ship
Being tossed and turned.
The sun sinks into the darkness
Of the night
And all is gone!

Charles Day (10)
Gretton Primary School

THE GOBLINS RETURNED

Along the passages they came,
Some were injured but none were lame,
Rambling along the tunnels dark,
Light nowhere not even a spark,
So sheltered there was never rain.

They were all unique none the same,
All were wild none were tame,
The smaller ones were wrapped in a cloak,
It was silent for no one spoke,
For the great Rondolf was to blame.

Only 2000 were to remain,
Of the rest who knows what became,
Then suddenly from behind there came a great shrieking,
Everyone, everyone squeaking
And there they lay dead again.

Flora Derounian (10)
Gretton Primary School

THE FROG

The pond was a glittering turquoise under the big green leaves.
The lush green grass was shining on the pond's verge.
The sun was beaming down onto the giant pond
   And the frog came leaping
      Leaping, leaping
The frog came leaping up to the still black fly.

Adam Parry (10)
Gretton Primary School

THE EARTH AND THE MOON

The Earth and the moon had a very long chat
One autumn night a long time ago.
The earth was boasting of his beautiful state
While all the moon could do was glow.

'My colours are bright brown, orange and red,
The leaves flutter gently and swirl round and round.
The hedges are full of colourful berries,
The trees rock in the wind and bow to the ground.

In the cold mist of morning dew glistens on my hair,
Children gather shining conkers on the way to school.
The golden fruit in the orchards are ready to be picked
And at midday the sunshine will show my glory to the full.'

The moon chuckled to herself as the earth rattled on
And said not a word as the winter came.
The earth was stripped of his glory and pride
Then had to hang his head in shame.

The earth cried out to the moon for help,
The earth was sorry for what it had said.
He shivered and stuttered as he talked
And the cold biting snow landed on his head.

The earth was freezing as the cold winds blew,
He was stripped of his beautiful leaves.
He started to cry as Jack Frost bit
And continued in spite of his desperate pleas.

Joseph Ogborn (11)
Gretton Primary School

THE SUN'S HERE

When I was out in the pool
The warm sun beamed on top of me.
I can hear the warm breeze
Whispering to me, sh, sh, sh.
I can see the trees waving
Side to side.
There's a light blue sky with
No clouds in sight.
Helicopters and planes
Dancing in the sky.
I can smell my dinner being cooked.
I can hear snakes hissing
In the midday sun.

Connor Snape (9)
Gretton Primary School

AUTUMN TREES

The wind is blowing
through the trees.
I can hear a rustling
in the leaves.

Light brown, dark brown,
everything is dead.
Next month
animals have to go to bed.

The leaves shudder
in the midnight darkness.
The winter is coming,
winter is coming.

Jenna Cornwell (10)
Gretton Primary School

THE CHEETAH AND THE GAZELLE

The sand was a glittering gold under the midday sun,
The sun was a powerful blaze up in the midday sky,
There was so little grass on the sandy plains,
And the cheetah came stalking,
stalking, stalking,
The cheetah came stalking up to the gazelle's tail.

The gazelle was grazing on a patch of grass,
its tail was swaying in the wind,
its hair was short and bristly coming off its long, long tail,
The cheetah came walking,
walking, walking,
The cheetah came walking up to the patch of grass.

The gazelle's ears were drooping, over its mane,
Everything was fine, no clouds were in the sky,
No sound could be heard on the sandy plains,
And then the cheetah started running,
running, running,
The cheetah started running up to its prey.

The gazelle was alert and lifted its head up high,
The gazelle saw a spotted figure coming,
On the sandy plains,
The gazelle saw the cheetah coming,
coming, coming,
It saw the cheetah coming and ran away to hide.

Jack Lawrence (8)
Gretton Primary School

THE MOUSE

The sun was a blaze of light.
The sky was light blue.
The leaves on the ground were blowing
along the dusty path.
The grass was glistening in the sun,
the ball was blue and shining.
The mouse came twitching,
twitching, twitching,
The mouse came twitching up
to the big barn door.

Hannah Jenkins (9)
Gretton Primary School

I HAVE TO DO A POEM

I have to do a poem . . .
But I can't think what to do . . .
I could do a poem about . . .
A robot on the moon,
A gorilla in a balloon.
A pig stuck in a tree,
The day I hurt my knee.
The day I lost a peg,
The day I broke my leg.
The day I learnt to hop,
The day I drank some pop.
The day I broke a table,
The day I wrote a fable
And my poem was about . . .
I'm still thinking!

Alice Elsmore (8)
Hambrook Primary School

RUNNING IN THE SUN

I am running in the sun,
It is not good for some,
I am rushing in the rain
Mum thinks it's a pain.
I am skipping in a storm
My friends are in the house, wrapped up warm.

I am playing in the snow
Without letting mum know!
I am flying in the wind
Watching as the children grinned.

Georgina Dunning (8)
Hambrook Primary School

SUMMER

It's nice and bright, the sun is shining,
It's hot, not cold, everyone's smiling.
The sand is burning and so are my feet,
There's donkey rides and ice cream to eat.
Then I go off for a little nap.
I wake up and I am fat.
Then I wake up for real and find it was just a dream,
And even my toes are nice and clean
And that's *The End!*

Rebecca Downes (8)
Hambrook Primary School

FIGHTING

F   ights are the worst things in the world.

I   don't like fights, someone gets hurt.

G   etting punched, kicked and fingers getting pulled back.

H   ave you ever got involved in a fight?

T   he school bell rings for going home today.

I   hope no one picks on me on the way home.

N   aughty children fighting in the road.

G   oing to bed and dreaming of fights!

Amy Callaway (8)
Hambrook Primary School

THE MILLENNIUM PARTY

Yippee! It's countdown to the New Millennium
3, 2, 1 Happy Millennium everyone!

We stared in amazement as fireworks blared out
with colours as bright as the moon.
The smell of gunpowder
Letting the fireworks shoot out of the ground
As it crackles through the air
Then suddenly they disappear.

The fear from a frightened cat
as it slowly paces its way back.
A chill of wind, cold in sight
People eating, enjoying the good
but out in the night people all over the world
Celebrating the year two thousand, 2000!

Matthew Holder (10)
Hesters Way Primary School

MY FAVOURITE ANIMALS

Oh, how I wish that I could see,
Dolphins swimming in the deep blue sea,
I dream of them at night,
Swimming in the ocean so bright,
Their twists and turns in the air,
Makes me want to stare and stare.

Oh, how I wish that I could see,
Tigers in the jungle watching me,
With your colours orange, black and white,
You are such an amazing sight,
Your stripes hide you in the bushes and trees,
Come out so that I can see you please!

Oh, how I wish that I could see,
A wonderful horse walking gracefully towards me,
With your colour chestnut brown,
Thinking of you never makes me frown,
With the wind blowing your mane from side to side,
We'll ride through the wind in the countryside.

Oh, how I wish that I could see,
A wild rabbit hopping free,
With your little twitching nose,
What you smell no one knows,
Your ears are so long,
You can hear the faintest bird song.

Oh, how I wish that I could see,
A chimpanzee swinging from tree to tree,
With your dinner of exotic fruit,
When you're eating you look so cute,
All the babies holding onto their mum,
Oh, look that one's sucking his thumb.

Adele Trevarthen (10)
Hesters Way Primary School

WHAT IS THAT?

The kettle boiled
Bubble, bubble
I hear footsteps
Tip-tap, tip-tap
The clock was ticking
Tick, tock
Windows banging
Bang, bang
Trees snapping
Crunch, crunch
Dogs barking
Woof, woof
Loud TV blurring
Zzzzzz, Zzzzzz
What is that?

Kevin White (10)
Hesters Way Primary School

THE MILLENNIUM PARTY

It's countdown to the New Millennium
5, 4, 3, 2, 1
It's a new century everyone.
Fantastic, amazing fireworks just about to explode.
Enormous fireworks banging in the air.
You can smell the burning of the rockets.
Fireworks spinning to the floor,
Black smoke flying in the air,
People shouting 'Happy Millennium' everywhere.

Larinda Ferguson (10)
Hesters Way Primary School

UP, UP AND AWAY

Up, up and away I'm going to the Moon today.
What will I see, a silvery sky
With twinkly gold bits or frosty stars
Twinkling from Mars!

Up, up and away I'm going to the Moon today,
I'm going in a rocket with twenty sockets
and the lights will flicker away.

Up, up and away I'm going to the Moon today
Was that a dog with more than four paws
Was that a two-headed alien I saw? I wonder . . .

Up, up and away I'm going to the Moon today,
The rocket sways as Earth fades away
I hold on tightly to my seat
I wonder who I might meet?

Up, up and away I'm going to the Moon today
Oh is that eyes looking at me?
I wonder if someone is spying on me.

Up, up and away I'm going to the Moon today
The higher it goes, it starts to feel like night
I hope great, big aliens don't want a fight.
Crash, Bang, Wallop
Boom!
I think I've made it to the *Moon!*

Sophie Maggs (10)
Hesters Way Primary School

THE MILLENNIUM PARTY

It's almost time for the Millennium party is about to start
The school closed for over a week,
Not worrying about my homework.
Looking forward to a New Millennium,
Party night, waiting, hoping.

It's Here

Watching the celebrations from all over the world
The music playing loud,
The beer going so quickly.
Musty gunpowder as the fireworks take off,
Silly string clinging to my face,
The lovely food bulging in my stomach
after feasting at my aunty's table.

The clock hand racing to 12 o'clock,
Everyone drinking red wine, getting drunk.
Party poppers going off with a great big *Bang!*
From far away all I could smell and see was . . .
Brightly coloured fireworks exploding in the sky.

Robert Pollard (10)
Hesters Way Primary School

LIFE IN THE NEW CENTURY

Robots doing all the things
that I don't want to do,
my homework and cleaning my bedroom.

Life deep, down under the sea,
beautiful rainbow fish and scaly, slimy crocodiles
swimming in the deep, dark sea.

Big, massive flying cars
whizzing through the wind.

Big, gold watches that can stop time
in any place at any time
only in God's hands.

Asa Hearn (10)
Hesters Way Primary School

OUR NEW CENTURY

People help others and there are no wars on the planet,
No teachers! Robots teach children in school,
No mean or drunk people who stab each other,
Cars, lorries and people floating in the air as gravity disappears,
Cars will be bigger, as long as seven metres long,
Boats can drive on land and float on the ocean.
Buildings as tall as 70 feet,
People make new transport for air, sea and road,
All people will be generous, polite and kind.
To come to life by putting computer chips in their head
We can understand fish, cats and dogs language in our New Century.

Lewis Trigg (10)
Hesters Way Primary School

THE INTERNET

An invention!
A discovery!
An amazing part of technology.

The Internet is its name
It gives many people
Much glory and fame.

It is loads of fun when you're surfing the Net
But with this type of surfing
You won't get wet.

The Net's good for learning
It is commonly used
It is great for all ages and keeps children amused.

There are loads of facts that you can find
There is loads of interesting stuff
That can be stored in your mind.

You can listen to music
There are games to play
You can go on the Net any time of day.

When you're on the Net
You can do some shopping
But it may be too hard to even try stopping!

If you don't have the Internet in your house
You can try the library
As long as you're quiet as a mouse.

Gemma Newbery (11)
Hesters Way Primary School

THE MILLENNIUM PARTY

Wow! It's countdown to the New Millennium,
5, 4, 3, 2, 1 Happy Millennium everyone!
The sound of sausages sizzling on the grill
The sound of fireworks booming off, all colourful.
The touch of a hot firework burning a child
See hot-dogs on the barbecue.
Taste a hot-dog all ready to eat
The sound of music very loud.

Laura Tovey (10)
Hesters Way Primary School

THE WIND

The spring wind is fresh
The summer wind is soft and sweet
The winter wind is strong
The autumn wind is mischievous
and sweeps the leaves along.

Sheree Rogers (9)
Moat Junior School

WINTER WIND

I hate the winter wind
It's just like Jack Frost
It stings my fingers
And my toes
It's like Jack Frost.

Lindsay Birch (9)
Moat Junior School

DON'T CALL SHARK SCARY FACE

Don't call shark scary face
Don't call shark skinny face
Don't call shark spiky face
Don't call shark grey face
Don't call shark all these rude words
Until you get out of the water.

Josh Rogers (8)
Moat Junior School

DON'T CALL

Don't call bear brown ears
Don't call bear sharp ears
Don't call bear spiky ears
Don't call bear scary ears
Don't say all these rude words
But wait till you go past the cave.

Kristen Nundy (7)
Moat Junior School

WINTER

W inter is when the snow falls from the sky
I   n the winter the leaves are gone
N o one knows why winter is here
T omorrow it will be winter again.
E   ven the birds will disappear
R   ivers are covered with solid ice.

Natasha Larby (11)
Moat Junior School

DESK AND CHAIR

Desk is square,
Desk is brown,
Desk has four legs
That touch the ground.

Chair is comfy,
Chair is neat,
Chair is somewhere
To park my seat.

School is great,
I go there.
In it you'll find
My desk and chair.

Jack Hayes (8)
Moat Junior School

CHRISTMAS TIME

C hristmas is a lovely time
H earts are filled with joy
R eindeers dance on the rooftops
I cicles hang from our noses
S tockings are hung at the end of our beds
T rees are decorated with lights
M istletoe hangs above the fire
A ngels sit on top of trees
S anta delivers presents to excited children

So I hope you enjoy Christmas!

Emma Heath (11)
Moat Junior School

CHRISTMAS HAS COME AGAIN

Christmas Eve has come at last,
the night I have been waiting for.
The year has seemed to go by fast
and Christmastime has come once more.
Christmas trees with hanging lights
which sparkle and twinkle through the nights.
Here comes Santa with his sleigh,
Heaped with parcels big and bright,
All his reindeers know the way,
Even in the dead of night.
Wake up early to go and see
what presents Santa has left for me.

Rachel Juby (10)
Moat Junior School

CHRISTMAS

The Christmas tree is standing still looking at decorations,
Children opening calendars saying it's nearly Christmas,
They can't wait to open presents and sing carols,
Oh but yum, yum we will eat Christmas dinner, then pud,
So now the Christmas tree is still looking at decorations,
Children open calendars and say eighteen nights to go then,
We get to open presents, sing carols,
Eat Christmas dinner, eat pud and say,
It's Christmas Day today,
Wahey!

Marissa Organ (10)
Moat Junior School

SILENT SNOWING

Outside of my window
It's snowing
It's cold and bitter
All the snowflakes are drifting
                                    slowly
                        down
                down
            down
I begin to look
Higher, higher
I see more flakes of snow
                                    slowly
                        down
                down
            down
The silent flakes
Begin to get smaller and smaller
The fluffy shapes begin to get
Slower and slower as the floating shapes
Begin to float
                                    slowly
                        down
                down
            down
To the dying ground.

Alisha Organ (11)
Moat Junior School

WHERE SNOW LANDS

Snow on my sandwich
Snow on my shoe
Snow on my swing
And on you and me.

Snow in my pond
Snow in my shed
Snow in my flowerbed
And on you and me.

Snow on the wall
Snow on the tree
Snow on the garden
And on you and me.

Emma Phillips (11)
Moat Junior School

CHRISTMAS

C   hristmas music playing
H   appy children singing
R   ighteous bells are ringing
I   n the town tonight.
S   anta comes down my chimney
T   oys and gifts please bring me
M   ay your reindeer guide you
A   nd may we always find you
S   afely on your way.

Sarah Black (11)
Moat Junior School

IN MY POCKET

In my pocket I found:
A twisted spoon
a 3D moon.
A piece of cake
a rattlesnake.
A big, old bear
a nose hair.
A big, fat elephant
a rotten plant.
A toy lighthouse
my pet mouse.
A clock of mine
a grapevine.

Stephen Best (10)
Moat Junior School

THE WEATHER IN THE AUTUMN

Monday it snowed, it seems ever so cold
the trees were like ice cream on a cone.
The leaves were all scattered
Like a colourful bed
And summer had gone and now was dead.
The conkers were falling off the trees
In their spiky shells.

Jessica Causton (10)
Moat Junior School

THE OLD, CREEPY CASTLE

There was an old, creepy castle,
in the castle there was a creaking . . .
as a zombie soldier,
who was ancient and skinny
came moaning and groaning,
down the stairs,
carrying his staff,
his eyes full of blood wrath.
There was a dripping . . .
as blood came from the damp ceiling
from the zombie's latest victim.
He had finished his unfinished business
he then lay in his coffin
to go to rest forever . . . (or so we think!)

Sam Vijay (9)
Moat Junior School

SINGING

Singing is good, singing is great
Singing is the bestest thing around.
Singing is good, singing is great
I love it very much.
I sing at night
I sing in bed
I sing in school
I sing in the shower
I sing at home
and I love it very much.

Michael Blackford (10)
Moat Junior School

CREEPY COTTAGE

I was in the bedroom,
there was . . .
a bent, broken bed,
a crooked, cramped chair and
a ripped teddy bear   poor thing!

I went in the bathroom,
there was . . .
weird, wacky water,
silly, slippery soap and
a deaf dog   poor thing!

I went in the kitchen,
there was . . .
three tiny tables,
a crooked, cracked cooker,
and a deaf dog   poor thing!

Katrina Locke (8)
Moat Junior School

REFUGEES

Here us say and say again for us refugees
We are in need.
We have not paid a single dime
but please love us all the time.
Someone, if you're out there, hear our cries,
For we are refugees crying for homes, clothes, food too.
Just hear our prayers, for refugees need you.

Sharlette Johnson (10)
Moat Junior School

THE SUN

The sun is a bright, golden eye
rising into the morning sky.
Up and down it rises
up, up and up into the sky.
The sunny times are coming, winter's gone
get ready, it's not cold any more.
Here comes the sun,
I will be able to go
and play in my garden again.
Down the slide, on the swing
up and down on the see-saw
riding round and round on my bike
racing up and down on my blades.
Weeeeeee!

Natasha Ogden (8)
Moat Junior School

FRIENDS

Sometimes we're friends
Sometimes we're not.
Sometimes we fight
Sometimes we don't
but we always have friends.
We have friends to share
to play with
and to keep secrets
but we all have friends for friendship's sake.

Natalya Gale (11)
Moat Junior School

THE ZOO

Whales swim under the water,
Whales are not there ready for slaughter.

Cats can purr very, very loudly
And they do it very, very proudly.

Sharks, when they swim their fin rises
And they're always ready to give surprises!

You like dogs, I like seals,
But we both wouldn't want to be a lion's meal!

Fish, they swim in the sea
And they aren't like you or me.

Giraffes, they stand at ten feet tall,
But you and me, we're really small.

But there is one creature that we are bigger
And that is a caterpillar.

James Carpenter (10)
Moat Junior School

I AM LONELY

I am lonely on my own
All around the playground
On my own
No one to play with
All alone.
Going around the playground
On my own.

Abigail Locke (10)
Moat Junior School

DR MEEOW'S PATIENTS

Dr Meeow's patients are big,
some are furry,
some are giants,
some are small,
some are quaint,
some are ugly,
some are wild,
some are tamed,
some are ashamed.
some are paid,
they stay in the shade.
some copy,
some have coffee,
some eat toffee,
some are shy,
some cry,
some eat rats,
some thing they're bats.

Ricky Breach (10)
Moat Junior School

SKIING

Skiing is good,
Skiing can be hard,
But you can get hurt badly.
You can get medals, just like me,
You have to work hard to get there
Like I have been for six years.
But now I am third in Europe
So I'm trying to get first
To beat everyone else.

Anouska Callander (11)
Moat Junior School

RABBITS

Rabbits are small
Rabbits are fluffy
Rabbits are chubby
Rabbits are cuddly
Rabbits are woolly
Rabbits are grey
Rabbits eat carrots and lettuce.

Sheniece Brown (10)
Moat Junior School

SUMMER TIME

Butterflies fluttering
Ice cream melting
Flowers popping out like the sun
Little insects jumping and bumping
Paddling pools shining
Birds singing.

Kevin Cox (9)
Moat Junior School

BIG BEAR

I was sitting in an old rocking chair,
When along came a big, scary bear,
I shouted and screamed
And the bear just beamed
And he ran off with my spare wig of hair.

Kimberley Woods (8)
Moat Junior School

CATS

Cats are furry and fluffy,
The colours come in all sorts,
Ginger, black, brown and white.
They sometimes have kittens.
They drink water and milk,
They eat cat food, fish, birds and mice.
They live in houses,
They sleep most of the time.
They like you to tickle their tummies,
They purr when they want feeding
And when they want you to stroke their rough tongues,
They come with pointy ears.
They come as a mammal,
But they don't come looking like a camel.

Victoria Scott (9)
Moat Junior School

ABOUT A DOG

My little puppy dog
It looks like gold.
It is cuddly
It eats meat
It chases cats
It sits on my lap.
It plays with me in the garden
It takes me for a walk
It wakes me up in the morning
It always jumps on me.

Gareth Peers (10)
Moat Junior School

THE TAP

Splitter, splatter,
the waterfall,
dripping on the metal sink.
Pitter, patter, plop,
splitter, splatter,
pitter, patter,
the water fell down the drain.
I couldn't handle that
pitter, patter,
splish, splash,
drip, drop,
plip, plop.
The tap still goes drip,
plaster up that hole!

Aaron Singh (9)
Moat Junior School

SOME PEOPLE THINK

Some people think they're really scary,
but actually they're really hairy.

Some people think there's something in the dark,
but actually that's my friend Mark.

Some people think they're really smart,
but actually they're just a tart.

Some people think they're really grand,
but actually they take all the land.

Jacqueline Jacobs (10)
Moat Junior School

THE CASTLE

In the creepy, old castle the ghost
went through the broken wall.
The door creaked silently
As the rotten skeleton came in.
The green zombie is running around the castle
going aooooh!
The lightning flashed around the castle then!
It broke the wall.

Owen Higgins (8)
Moat Junior School

GOLDEN SUN

Rising sun ever so high
Midnight comes, he says goodbye.
Just like the golden fire he keeps us warm
Trying to get rid of that rainy storm.
Whenever you see a golden sky
Look up at the sun it'll never die.

Karl Holland (8)
Moat Junior School

GOLD

The gold sun comes up today,
Tomorrow it shall shine and stay,
It's rich and warm, what a wonderful sun,
Hope it stays many years to come.
The warmth, the warmth, I'm so, so glad,
The fading sun is going down today,
Goodnight sun it's time to fly away.

Natasha Phillips (9)
Moat Junior School

CREEPY CASTLE

Dripping . . .
      as the
            blood drips
                from the vampire.

Cooking . . .
      as the
            old witch
                cooks mouse pie.

Clashing . . .
      as the
            devil smashes
                cups on a butler.

Smash! . . .
      as the
            wolf-man smashes
                into the wall.

Sucking . . .
      as the
            bat sucks blood
                from the wolf-man.

The bats are thirsty, the bats are think
The door is open, so come on in.

Josh Merrett (9)
Moat Junior School

THE WATERFALL

Dirty water comes thundering madly down the fall
and into the boiling lake,
which makes the little fish shake madly.

Big tidal waves come down the river and into the chilly lake,
which makes the little fish shiver badly.

The big waterfall freezes,
the fish freeze too!

Joseph Critchley (9)
Moat Junior School

ZOMBIE

I was singing in my royal bedroom,
When a zombie came out with a boom,
I said 'Who are you?'
Ran out of the gloom,
And now he is still in that room.

Karina Clutterbuck (9)
Moat Junior School

HORROR

I was surfing on the loo
when a zombie came with goo
so I said 'Get out quick
or I will hit you with a brick'
and I scared him off with a
Boo!

Paige Satherley (8)
Moat Junior School

WHAT HAVE I GOT TO WORRY ABOUT

(Inspired by Children's Hospital)

I wonder what's for tea?
Maybe I can watch TV.
What have I got to worry about?

The baby whose insides were out of its tummy,
He must have a worried mummy.
What have I got to worry about?

The girl who's lost her mum and dad,
She must be very, very sad.
What have I got to worry about?

The boy that lives on bread and rice,
He must be wanting something nice.
What have I got to worry about?

The lad that lies on a special bed,
With nuts and bolts through his head.
What have I got to worry about?

The children who live with war all around,
It must be a frightening sound.
What have I got to worry about?

Maybe I'll go out to play
At the end of another day.
What have I got to worry about?

Daniel Walker (10)
Moat Junior School

Colour Rapt

My hair is brown, my eyes are blue,
The TV is black, the tree is green.
My desk is full of different colours.
My CD player is silver, the fireplace is gold,
Now my desk is tidy, where are my colours?

My house is full of different colours,
Pink, purple, green, blue.

Jennifer Heath (8)
Moat Junior School

You Make Me Feel

You make me feel like a big, hot air balloon,
You make me feel like a silly cartoon,
You make me feel like a pin,
You make me feel like I want to throw myself in the bin,
You make me feel like a big ear,
You make me feel like I'm here.

Danielle Gordon-Waugh (9)
Moat Junior School

Leaf

The leaf is so green.
It has lines down the middle.
It is dark, dark green.

Daniel Vijay (7)
Moat Junior School

SPIDERS' REVENGE

If your house is dirty,
or if your house is clean,
the spiders will come back again
because they are so mean.
Your house will be attacked
when you turn your back.
Watch out, there might be a gang
They might make a bang.

There might be a fright
from the spiders in their spite.
They play on your head
and sometimes at the bottom of your bed.
So don't flush them down the drain
because they will come back again.

Collette Peers (9)
Moat Junior School

BLUE

The sky's so blue
It looks like new,
So is the sea
That splashes me.

Blue is the colour
Of the hat
My mum wore
To see 'Take That'.

Anne Carpenter (8)
Moat Junior School

BOOM!

When I go to bed, it's as silent as can be,
Then suddenly, I hear in the garage,
Banging and clanging,
  Crackling and sizzling,
    Tapping and pinging,
      Tumbling and rumbling,
        Coming and going,
                Boom!

Rebecca Allen (8)
Moat Junior School

WHAT A GOAL

Football is fun,
Football is loud,
Football is rough,
Football is hard,
Football is muddy,
Then Leeds score a lovely goal
And everybody's cheering
And everybody is happy.

Robert Folley (10)
Moat Junior School

SPAGHETTI

Spaghetti, spaghetti, nice and hot,
Squirming like worms all over the pot.
Spaghetti, spaghetti, I love it a lot,
Spaghetti, spaghetti, don't get in a knot.

Emma Willetts (10)
Moat Junior School

DR RENT-A-MOUTH MOUTHS

Some are loud,
some are found,
some fade,
but they have been made.

Some are quiet,
some are loud,
some fly off the ground,
some chatter all around,
some are even crowned.

Some smell,
some tell,
some have a pan
and hit my gran.
Some do raps
and see a rat.

Some are shy,
some cry,
some die,
some stay alive.

Some are fat
so they sit on mats.

Aaron Lee (7)
Moat Junior School

FOOTBALL

Football here,
Football there,
Football's nearly everywhere.
The goals are up, the grass is green
And all is ready for a game.

The whistle blows
And off we go.
Henry rung sup the line,
Trips, falls and breaks his arm.
He's off the pitch, we're down a man,
I think we need a substitute.

It's half-time,
They are up 2-0,
All we need is a miracle.
We'll fight again in the second half.
Coach brought us all an energy drink.

A few minutes later we're back on the pitch,
Raring to go and score.
Five minutes later it came true,
The miracle finally came.
The best player came jogging onto the pitch
And scored three goals, and we won!

Michael Rogers (10)
North Cerney CE School

THE ANNOYING HABITS OF POTTY POLITICIANS

If there was a prize for the most annoying person,
the politicians would win it hands down . . .

They're potty and dotty,
snotty and mad,
their brains are like jelly
and they're also quite sad
to even start the job in the first place!

The Government has billions to spend,
from the NHS to the Navy,
but they still don't know,
after years of practice,
how to make proper school gravy!

Jamie Salazar (11)
North Cerney CE School

DEATH

Blood and guts are flying,
Many people here are dying,
Carcasses of ashes,
Plans that keep on crashing,
All the people lashing, lashing out.
Why war?
Why not a game?
Those villainous people with guns,
Killing just for fun.

Kelly Moy (10)
North Cerney CE School

THE WORLD COULD BE BETTER

There are poor people in the world
As everyone knows.
There's money in the world,
As everyone knows.
It's being spent on roads and buildings,
Not on animals, trees or the countryside around.
Why can't we spend the money more fairly?
Food for the needy,
Electricity for the poor,
Clothes for the homeless,
Peace so everyone can live together.
As everyone knows,
The world could be better.

Huw Rettie (11)
North Cerney CE School

POKÉMONS

Pokémon here, Pokémon there, Pokémon everywhere.
There's Pikachu, Golem, Sandslash, Nidoking, Bellsprout, Vulpix
Gotta catch 'em all,
Oddish, Ditto Voltorb,
Ash, Gary, Brock, Misty.
And they're all so cool.

Robert Gardiner (10)
North Cerney CE School

MORNING

It's Saturday morning
And it's just dawning
But I'm still yawning
The cock's going to crow
But in my bed I'm going to lie
No work, no school, it's Saturday!

William Seymour & Ben Barton (9)
North Cerney CE School

ANIMAL EPITAPHS

Here lies the body
Of a microscopic flea,
Sadly he was flattened
By a vicious, frozen pea!

Here lie the bones
Of a huge, colossal toad,
Tragically run over
On a never-ending road!

Here lies the body
Of an enormous iguana,
Sadly he died
In the country of Yugoslavia.

Here lie the bones
Of a cheeky, brown monkey,
Sadly he was trampled
By an angry black donkey!

Daniel Hilder (11)
Northleach CE Primary School

A New Millennium

M y favourite part
I   n the last millennium was when the new one came.
L   ots of people were crowding around,
L   oads of balloons stacked above us,
E   veryone shouting excitedly and happily,
N   ow there are loads of sparkling, whirling fireworks
                                    blasting in the dark sky.
N   o one's missing them.
I   nside are the remains of party poppers and balloons
                                    that have just been popped.
U   nder the dark sky, people are thinking
M   oments nobody would want to miss.

Fay Davies (11)
Northleach CE Primary School

The Sea

When I wake each morning I sweep the bay.
Beneath me, the coral sways as shoals of
                                    colourful fish swim by.
In the day when the boats come out
They are my toys, but also my enemies.
When I get vexed I punch at the rocks
Until they fall tumbling.
I am a magnet for all sea creatures,
Crustaceans from small to big.
At the end of every day I stretch along the shore.

Thomas See (11)
Northleach CE Primary School

What I Like About Sleep

The very warm and snug of it,
The horrible bed bugs of it,
The wonderful cool feel of it,
The different shapes and wheels of it,
The soft duvet and sheets of it,
The way you can find feet in it!

Jessica Wills (10)
Northleach CE Primary School

What I Like About My Pet

The silky, shiny fur of it,
The funny, fuzzy purr of it,
The teeny, tiny paws of it,
The careful, climbing claws of it.

Dominic Higgs (10)
Northleach CE Primary School

What I Like About My Cat

The fuzzy, fizzy hair of it,
The kindness and the care of it,
The tiny, teeny paws of it,
The shiny, whiny claws of it.

Adam Hubbard (11)
Northleach CE Primary School

MILLENNIUM

M illennium
I s a thousand years
L ots of people celebrating all over the world,
L ots of fireworks go in the air, they are all different colours,
E veryone celebrates,
N ew millennium,
N ow it is two thousand,
I t is going to be a great time in two thousand.
U ntil we all count down to the new
M illennium.

Kim Welch (10)
Northleach CE Primary School

MILLENNIUM

M illennium eve
I had a party.
L ots of people came
L aughing and
E choing through the
N ight.
N oisy friends
I n our home
U ntil two o'clock in the
M orning.

Luke Dooner (11)
Northleach CE Primary School

THE SEA'S STORY

I've been here for centuries,
I've seen people evolve.
I've rocked people in boats and on surfboards.
Rocks pierce my swaying body.
I crash across the shining beach.
As people leave and it becomes dark,
I devour the motionless shore.
I rescue the marooned crabs and shells.
My sapphire-blue body rests until the next day.
When I wake, I stretch my glistening body.
I start lapping the beach.
My crystal clear body will last for centuries more.

James Binns (11)
Northleach CE Primary School

MILLENNIUM

M ilestone in time, celebrated,
I   n a big way,
L   oads of fireworks light up the sky!
L   ittle children cry, cry, cry.
E   veryone's happy.
N ew millennium,
N ew beginning for mankind.
I   n different countries,
U nder the stars the
M illennium is soon to strike.

Jonathan Salmon (11)
Northleach CE Primary School

MILLENNIUM

M illennium
I s one thousand years
L ots of crackling, sparkling fireworks exploding in the air
L ots of wonderful colours from the fireworks
E veryone laughing and cheering,
N eighbours having parties for the
N ew Year
I t is really exciting watching
U nusual fireworks
M illennium

George Chilton (10)
Northleach CE Primary School

MILLENNIUM

M illennium
I s a thousand years
L ovely fun it was
L ots of fireworks
E verything was beautiful
N obody knew it was going to be good when it happened
N ew millennium is here
I had champagne on the night
U nited Kingdom celebrated on a Friday night
M illennium was lovely

Dean Wharton (11)
Northleach CE Primary School

WHAT I LIKE ABOUT MY CHINCHILLA

The fuzzy, fluffy hair of it,
The cuddly, touchy care of it,
The big and mouse-like ears of it,
The hissing noise and fears of it.

Jordan Miller (11)
Northleach CE Primary School

THE RIVER SEVERN

Looking out of my bedroom window
I can see the river flowing swiftly past.
It is muddy and dredgers come to clear it
To make it flow so fast.

There are boats going up the river all the time,
Some have discos and I can hear the music from my bed.
Barges go up the river, one has a water wheel and
some are painted red.
Grain is carried by tankers and tugs
And I wave to the drivers drinking tea from their mugs.

There are lots of animals on the river and the banks,
Swans, a heron, a cormorant and ducks big and small.
The nasty mink is a danger to them all

In spring a big wave which is called the Severn Bore
Sweeps up fish and elvers, rubbish and lots more.
The river is full of marvellous things,
So come and see the animals with wings.

Emily Meadows (9)
Norton CE Primary School

GORILLAS

Munching, crunching bamboo reeds,
always climbing up the trees,
ferocious though you can be,
some of you would never hurt a flea.
Clenching your fists, punching your chest
making the most hilarious noise,
I wonder if you would like to play with toys.
The rainforest is home to you,
your children are playing peek-a-boo.
You nest in the trees,
but do you pay your fees?
You're very close to us,
so never catch the bus
. . . and leave us!

Charlotte Pritchard (10)
Norton CE Primary School

THE TIGER

The tiger is king of the jungle,
Proud he is as he runs in and around.
Orange fur, big thick stripes and very sharp claws.
He lives in Asia and he is strong to fight.
Big jungle trees he sniffs.
When the sun begins to set, he starts to lie down to rest.
Morning comes and he wakes up in time for hunting,
Then you see him yawn and those big teeth.

Michelle Keel-Stocker (9)
Norton CE Primary School

OUR GARDEN

I like our garden
      when
the sun is singing a sunny song
      when
the rain is dancing a rainy dance
      and
the scent floating around smells beautifully green

The feelings feel good
      when
the undergrowth hums a melody
      when
the leaves rustle and chatter
      and
the primroses are whispering a tune.

I breathe the air of the garden
The beautiful garden with millions of prizes.

Claire Overal (10)
Norton CE Primary School

WINTER

W hiteness all across the land
I   vy covered in snow
N ose red in winter coldness
T oes so cold that they hurt when you wriggle them
E venings darken soon after school
R ed berries stripped from their trees by hungry birds

Simon Curtis (9)
Norton CE Primary School

FLYING FEVER

I'm going on holiday,
High up in the air,
It's my first time flying,
And I'm in for a scare.

I'm at the airport,
An hour to wait,
I am so nervous,
I hope that the plane's not late.

The plane is all ready,
It's time to board,
I need to say my prayers,
So *please help* me Lord.

We're all belted in,
And ready to go,
Take a deep breath and . . .

Up, up and
    Away we
        Go!

Sophie Brammer (11)
Norton CE Primary School

FOOTBALL CRAZY

Football, football on the ground,
Football, football, ever so round,
Football, football, like my head,
Football, football, sometimes red,
Football, football, better than hockey,
Football, football, or shall I be a jockey?

Zeb D-Matty (10)
Norton CE Primary School

THE BUG

There was a little bug,
Deep under ground,
Dressed up as a grub,
He squirmed without a sound.

While sun bathing on his towel,
He suddenly saw a trowel,
'Please don't laugh
I might get cut in half.'

Clambering through the dirt,
He met his friend called Bert,
Off they went to find a flowerpot,
And hide behind a snowdrop.

Jonathan Biruls (10)
Norton CE Primary School

POLAR BEAR

My polar bear
Has no hair
And I don't care.
When he eats fish
He sometimes would wish
For more fish, fish, fish.
We love him though and he
Sometimes throws big
Tempers,
Just like me . . .

Amy Davis (9)
Norton CE Primary School

THE LONELY CHICK(EN)

I just can't wait,
I'm going to be ate,
there's a party tonight.
Oh my God, I look a fright,
all burnt at the edges,
I look worse than potato wedges.

All set on the tables.
Oh no, they've arrived and are looking at the labels,
the spicy hot sauce.
Yippee, I'm the main course.
They're putting me with rice,
hmmm, actually they look quite nice.

A boy with his fork,
oh no, he stops to talk.
He finally digs in,
yes, I win.
He's left me on his plate,
but now it's too late.

But who is this? Another grin
with a very hairy chin.
She picks me up and in I go,
I just go with the nearest flow.
I floated down into her tummy,
now I know I must have been yummy.

Emilie Dill (10)
Norton CE Primary School

MY MAGIC BOX

I will put in the box
the hanging vine from the first rainforest,
water from the biggest tidal wave,
the pump of blood going around the heart.

I will put in the box
the biggest iceberg ever in the cold Antarctic,
a chip from the oldest fossil,
a jumping grasshopper on a summer's day.

I will put in the box
every single country from Africa to Antarctica,
the ruby from the biggest and oldest temple,
the ripest fruit from the Caribbean.

I will put in the box
an extra life for all kinds of animals or humans,
The scattered, starry sky in midnight blue atmosphere,
the bright coloured lava from an erupting volcano.

I will put in the box
gold-coloured leaves from an autumn morning,
cotton wool clouds from the sky above,
the purring of my cat as he sleeps by the fire.

I shall snowboard in my box,
speeding over the mountains of Switzerland,
Flying over a fluffy cliff,
The colour of a polar bear swimming in a frozen sea.

Jack Lewis (9)
Norton CE Primary School

DOCTOR DOCTOR

Doctor doctor
come to me
please be quick
I have broken my knee.

> Doctor doctor
> make it better
> because if you don't
> it is sure to fester.

Doctor doctor
now you've been
my knee is better
I can now spring clean.

Katie Fox (11)
Norton CE Primary School

SEAGULL

As swift as the sea,
flying higher than a bee,
the seagull swoops down for its prey.

He dives down under
and starts to wonder
which meal he'll bring up to the bay . . .

Charles Neveu (9)
Norton CE Primary School

DOLPHINS

D olphins are nice, very nice indeed, you can ride
   on them if you please.
O h! You will have so much fun with them.
L lollipops, ice creams, take them to the show.
P lotting what to do, if you listen you can hear them.
H ide where they can't find you, come and see the fun.
I n the water come and look, can you see them through
   the loops.
N oise dolphins talk, talk, talk
   Sometimes I think they want to walk.
S ometimes I want a pet.
   I would like one that's wet.

Harriette Gardner (8)
Norton CE Primary School

YOU AND LITTLE ME

You and little me
flying in the clouds high above the sea.
You and little me
drinking our gone-off tea.
You and little me
wishing to God we had the key,
the key of light for
you and little me.

Piers Neveu (10)
Norton CE Primary School

MUFFIN THE CAT

Muffin the cat is small and sweet,
Whiskas is what she likes to eat.
She lives under the bed,
Her collar is red
And everyone says, 'How cute.'

She chases her toy mouse round the room,
Until Mummy comes in with a big black broom.
She's scared and runs out
So we all shout,
'Muffin, come back in this room!'

Black, gold and white,
In her flight
Right across the garden,
We say 'Pardon,'
As she goes to the loo!
Don't do a poo.

She likes eating flies,
'Miaow' she cries,
The tabby with an attitude.

Little white paws
And sharp jaws.
Little white chest,
She's the best.

Karina Withers (9)
Norton CE Primary School

BRUM

I have a green car called Brum, which is made of wood.
He drives so far for such a little car.
In his boot is his battery and motor, in the front he has a little
hooter.
He has a little steering wheel, and lights for in the dark, I often
drive him around the village hall our park.
He has four blown up tyres and a clock to tell the time.
He has two brakes, but one is fake.
His seat is made of leather, which feels as soft as a feather. It
goes backwards and forwards to suit everyone, it even comes out
to fit in my mum.

Alice Pickering (9)
Norton CE Primary School

SPRINGTIME

In the spring, flowers sprout, then their petals open out.
Fleecy lambs skipping past their woolly rams.
The woolly rams call their fleecy lambs to come and eat
The juicy dewdrop grass.
Sweet smelling daffodils dance their way in the warm
Sunlit hours.
Now it's night you have to be quiet.
The daffodils close their petals and the lambs curl up and
Go to sleep.
Night! Night!

Katie Hawkins (9)
Norton CE Primary School

THE HUMAN BODY

A long time ago there was
a archaeologist who had
discovered the human body.
He saw lots of bones
all over the place.
His camp in the jungle
far, far, away. When he
got back he put all the
bones together to make
a human body.
He had these plastic
organs he took so long
to put them together
then he started to make names
for the organs.
He made names like Ozam
Brozam, Sozam, Dozam and lots
of funny names that rhyme
with Ozam.
He joined the skull bone to the
cheek bone to the collar bone
to the back bone to the hip bone
to the toe bone.
Finally he had finished putting
the bones together and after he
had to put the organs in the body
Once he had done that he was just
relaxing in a nearby river.

Colin McKechnie (10)
Norton CE Primary School

THE SCORPION

It was late at night,
When I had a fright,
In bed at night.
It was crawling in my bed,
Shivers running through my head,
In bed at night.
I had a little tickle,
While eating some pickle,
In bed at night.
I was putting on my socks,
When I heard something in a box,
Early in the morning.
I saw it, it is black and brown,
It bites, not very nice, with a hard shell.
But I won't see it much more because
I sent him to Hell.

Matthew Karlsson (9)
Norton CE Primary School

I LIKE ART

I like art in every way
Cloudy colours shining my way
The colours are like angels on clouds
Floating birds, rainbows over streams.

I dream about colours, think about
Colours, all that I can see
I love art and that's me.

Mellissa Holland (8)
Norton CE Primary School

PIRANHAS

Neither feet or arms have I
But I have fins.
And I use teeth, teeth, teeth.

Neither shell or claws have I
But I have big eyes to watch my prey and think
When the right time to strike is.
And I use teeth, teeth, teeth.

Neither horns or nose have I
But I have a special scanning system.
And I use teeth, teeth, teeth.

Neither wings or beak have I
But I have gills so I can breathe under water.
And I use teeth, teeth, teeth.

I am master of my teeth, so I can kill my prey.
And I use teeth, teeth, teeth.

Alex Pritchard (8)
Norton CE Primary School

SPRING

S   pring is warm, full of flowers
P   oppies, daffodils, rabbits and sheep
R   eally loud birds, twitter and twitter
I   n spring children go out to play with a
    smile on their faces.
N   ice sunshine really bright
G   eece swimming in the lake.

Sian Owen (8)
Norton CE Primary School

DOLPHINS

Dolphins wow, they're my favourite animals
I like to feel their rubbery grey skin
I like to see them splash water, dive and jump at shows
I like to hear them make those funny noises.

I like to see them swim and glide gracefully
Through the clear and still water.
I like to feed and throw them fish.
I always know where a dolphin is because I can
See its rubbery grey fin going up and down in
The sunlight.

Lauren Francis-Smith (9)
Norton CE Primary School

MATHS

Maths is great and fun,
It feels good when you're done.

Maths is good for the brain,
Even if it drives you insane.

Maths is really good for the mind,
Just can't wait when I divide.

Maths is the best subject in the world,
So come on and give it a whirl.

Kirsty Brammer (11)
Norton CE Primary School

CHRISTMAS

C hildren running about on Christmas eve.
H appy children opening their presents.
R eindeers flying in the sky.
I wonder what is in there.
S anta saying 'Merry Christmas to all the people.'
T hank you for my presents Santa.
M erry Christmas and a happy new year.
A nd mince pies for Rudolph.
S o he leads the way home.

Stephanie Brammer (9)
Norton CE Primary School

DINOSAURS

Dinosaurs are big and small,
Thick skinned to avoid death,
Glowing eyes to see in dark,
They can be fat or thin,
Razor teeth to tear chunks of meat,
They run fast to catch their prey,
Pointed tails to whip prey,
But one day they'll become
Unknown.

Oliver Gamston (8)
Norton CE Primary School

GOLDFISH

Fish have no ears.
They eat so much.
Goldfish swerve up and down and around.
All fish have to live in a fish tank or a pond.
Goldfish have very shiny orange coats.
All fish make big bubbles.
Goldfish are so funny when you have to
Clean their fish tank out.
You can have so much fun with goldfish.

Hannah Warren (8)
Norton CE Primary School

FOOTBALL

Football crazy, that's me.
Officials of the game know a lot.
Ow! I just broke my ankle.
The game of two halves.
Barmy about it, my friends are.
Always watching it on Sky.
Lovely and muddy.
Loving every minute of it.

Thomas Fox (8)
Norton CE Primary School

FAIRIES

Fairies sing songs of love
And dance around the moon for joy
I've seen their glittering wings
Sparkle in the moonlight
I've seen them run back to their flowers
Or trees I have, I have, I have
Seen the *Fairies!*

Lily-Mae Szewczuk (7)
Norton CE Primary School

CATS

I love cats, they're elegant and cute,
The Siamese, Japanese and oriental blue
Scratching at the door is it the postman or
The milkman or maybe it's the cat!
Miaow!

Laura Overal (7)
Norton CE Primary School

AT SEA

I was sailing on the stormy sea
My brother sitting next to me
A lovely boat coloured blue and red
A sailing boat all made of wood
The sun was shining in the sky
The seagulls flying high
Filling me with joy.

Matthew Whittle (9)
Overndale School

VALENTINE TREE

Love is forgiveness,
If I make a mess,
Love is milk and bread,
Before I go to bed.

Love is a kiss,
When away my mum I miss,
Love is a cuddle,
In bed with her I huddle.

Love is happiness,
The greatest gift I possess,
Love is to give,
It's something that can't be sieved.

Love is not honey,
Or a surprise party,
Love is care,
Like my teddy bear.

Robert Figueiredo (10)
Overndale School

THE WIND

As the wind flows through the air
There's a feel of a light breeze coming
I can see it whizzing and whooshing
And the sound of it humming.

I hope it's not a hurricane
That's going to blow a gale
Or an enormous frightening twister
Causing havoc with its tail.

Kate Reynolds (9)
Overndale School

A VALENTINE

Love is caring when I have done
something wrong.
Love is sun-shining through the
break of dawn.
Love is forgiveness that does not
need money.
Love is something surprising and
can also be funny.
Hugs and a kiss,
These are things I hope I'll never
miss.
Being happy, being good,
Love is not chocolates.
Love is just the way it should be.
Love is in the air
Love is always fair.
Love is something very special.
Showing that you care.

Zuwena Reid-Bailey (10)
Overndale School

THE SKY'S THE LIMIT

While gazing into the dark night sky,
I saw a spaceship go flashing by,
It stood out clearly by the light of the moon,
But going too fast it was gone all to soon.

While all of a sudden it came whizzing back,
I thought to myself, what is that?
It was round in shape and tall in height,
It went flying past me and I jumped
In fright.

Hannah Woods (10)
Overndale School

THE WIND

As the wind may
Howl and roar
It may blow the tree
To knock at the door

A tornado goes
Round and round
It makes a noise
That is a horrible sound

A hurricane
Can lift up things
Like on the top
Of those dustbins

The wind is cool
And it blows
I do not like it
When it howls.

Laura Ridley (9)
Overndale School

BUMBLE BEE

It has sting,
But does not sing,
Collects pollen to the lot,
And stored in a pot.

It likes nectar from a flower,
Which gives it power,
It likes the petals,
But not water from kettles.

It lives in a hive,
And is always alive,
There's a room for the queen,
Who is very mean.

James Dimond (9)
Overndale School

VALENTINE POEM

Love is forgiveness
To make you happy
Love is to talk
When you're feeling down.

Love is to give
Great and small
Love is to care
For your friends and all.

Love is to be cuddled
When you're scared
Love is to kiss
To show you cared.

Luke Goulden (9)
Overndale School

SLIMY

I'm slimy and ugly
And really, really fat.
I am behind you
And I'll take your hat.

I eat people's bones
I eat all their skin
I eat fish
But not their fins.

I'm made of slime
And very green
I've got very big ears
But I've never been seen.

I go in lots of places
I do not like the rain
I go out in the sun
I've got a brain.

Abigail Britton (7)
Overndale School

ROCKET

Rockets have fuel
They are not light
After the countdown
Stars are bright.

Rockets go high
Rockets go low
They go to the Moon
And they glow.

Eleanor Luffman (7)
Overndale School

MY BROTHER DOMINIC

My brother always calls me ugly,
I just smile and call him chubby.
Then he'll start to punch and kick.
I'll just say to him, 'Dom you're thick.'

When Mum and I watch TV,
He will say very quietly,
Come on then, you ugly elf,
I'll say, 'Dom, you're talking to yourself.'

In the kitchen I'll ask Mum,
'Oh please, can I have a yummy ice bun.'
Then my brother will say to the cat,
'Watch her eating, she will get fat.'

I'll ask him a question and he will just say,
'Shut up you idiot, otherwise I'll make you pay.'
Then my mum will tell him off,
Tell her normally, you stupid troff.

So that's my brother, isn't he nice,
I guess you could say he's no sugar and spice.
He's a bit of a thug as you can see,
But why does he have to bully me.

Olivia Burgess (11)
Querns School

THE BOY WHO SAW THE GHOUL

There was a boy who had a dream
Which very nearly made him scream
He got up as the day was dawning
And in the middle of him yawning
He thought he saw a real live ghoul
Saying 'I want to go to school'.

The boy went to school the following day
And just as he was going out to play
He thought he saw the same real ghoul
Swimming, in the swimming pool
What was that boy's really scary dream
That very nearly made him scream?

James Lossin (9)
Querns School

MILLENNIUM

I'm a true millennium child
We have lots of fun: we really go wild.
Surgeons can replace a mangled leg,
And I e-mail my friends each night on the web.

Millennium night I remember so well.
It was just like being cast in a spell.
Bangs and crashes, lasers, bright light.
Filled the sky that particular night.

I rode on the Ferris wheel,
And went into the Dome.
We were there for ages.
I didn't want to go home.

Rivers and seas, the earth and the breeze,
No one play with nature, please!
The birds and the animals are ours to protect,
For the future generations to guard and respect.

People are wondering about 3001.
The future is here,
It's really begun!

Gabriella Swaffield (11)
Querns School

FLYING

I fly so high,
With my eagle's eye,
And no one will catch me,
I see my prey, far, far away,
Like the villain sees his.

I swoop down upon my catch,
We exchange a quick look,
As if to say,
See you another day.

His confidence annoys,
For no one escapes,
From my matured sleek body,
As it activates,
Talons whip out from underneath
The silky hand.

Now the battle is over,
But none will ever see,
How on earth I killed him,
Because of my agility.

Nicholas Dobson (11)
Querns School

CHRISTMAS

Christmas has come once again
And all the children are waiting
Waiting at home sat round a flame
They hear the bells in the sky
They look out of the window
And see Santa fly by.

Santa is on his way in his
Golden, shiny sleigh.
Oh look there's Rudolph, what shall
We say.
The children run out and what a
Good sight.
All the children with joy, it's just
Great.

Anastasia Asprou (10)
Querns School

SHH! SHH!

Shh! Shh! Can't you hear
Someone quick come over here.
Something's moving . . .over there
Oh please come now it'll give me a scare.

Shh! Shh! It's reached the hollow
Shall I stay or shall I follow
Now it's gone! I wonder why?
Perhaps this thing can really fly.

Shh! Shh! Can't you hear?
Those footsteps really are quite clear
What's that perfume I can smell?
It seems familiar, I know it well.

It's big, it's tall,
With clothes and all
I shall hide under cover.
Gosh! It's only Mother.

Christabel Blanch (10)
Querns School

MY PONY

My pony, he's such fun to ride
He has a lovely pace and stride
Racing against the rolling hills
His heart is full of warmth and thrills

At midnight when he rears so high
His nose appears to touch the sky
The late night birds fly high and low
Before he gives his final blow
And falls into a long, deep sleep
Not opening his eyes for a final peep.

I love my pony from head to toe
And he loves me, I surely know.

Laura Tyler (10)
Querns School

THE YEAR 2000!

Rockets shooting through the air
Catherine wheels that give you a scare
Colours shooting everywhere
Every direction, here and there

Roman candles twirling round
Making such a wonderful sound
Falling, falling, falling like rain
Then another shoots up again

Slowly but surely the ending of fun
The fireworks finish now everything's done
Now we're waiting for next year to come
Then it will be 2001!

Eleanor Field (9)
Querns School

DYING

When I die
I'll come right back
As a skeleton or a vampire bat
I won't really perish in my grave
But scare people, see if they're
Brave.

I'll eat flesh in the dead of night
If people walk by
I'll give them a fright

It's really cool
Being a ghost
Because you can always visit the
past.

I'll scare people in the
Neighbourhood
Tap at the windows
Scrape at the wood
I'll even visit the tomb of the
Dead
I'll have a chat with Uncle Fred

Now I've learnt
It's quite fun dying
Don't be unhappy, don't start
Crying.

William Slator (10)
Querns School

OVER THE WALL

Over the wall far, far away
There could be a cloud on a
Sunny day.

The crispy old leaves come
A drifting
Down,
Yellowish, reddish and dirty
Brown.

The colours of autumn are
Like burnished
Gold,
As bright as the sun or so I'm
Told
They lie on the lawn, a carpet
Of leaves
Waiting to play in a swirling
Breeze.

Emily Bush (9)
Querns School

DOLPHIN

I live among the fishes
Which swim in a glittering mass
They twist and turn and shimmer,
A million krill and rass.

I leap out of the water
My flippers twist and flail
I plunge back underwater
Ooh! and Flipper's grabbed my tail.

My fins have sliced through water,
My jaws have clamped round fish
I've never eaten seaweed,
But fish's a brilliant dish.

Harry Frost (10)
Querns School

SEASONS

Spring!
So beautiful and bright
Look as a bird takes flight.
You see the fledglings in the air,
You see them fall and say,
'It's not fair!'

Summer!
I love the summer sun.
Why is there only one?
The holidays!
The end of the school year is near.

The leaves are falling through the air,
Look at the birds here and there!
The leaves are so pretty,
Why do they go?
It's such a pity.

Winter!
Look at the snow!
Please don't go.
It's Christmas time!
Are those gifts all mine?

Georgina Greenwood (9)
Querns School

TEA

Listen, listen, listen to me,
Don't be afraid or run up a tree,
It's me you know,
Please come with me,
To the hollow in the willow tree.

Step inside, stay for tea,
Make yourself comfy, coffee or tea?
Milk with sugar? Black or white?
Sit down Tabby, you'll give her a fright.

Sandwich or biscuit? A gingerbread snap?
Sponge cake or lemon tart?
Strawberries for start,
Cream on the side,
Sugar if you wish,
Sorry about that, here's a dish.

The weather's much hotter,
The sun seems to shine,
The rain has stopped coming,
Everything's fine.

It's time to go now,
Things have been great,
Please don't pine,
My darling Kate.

Luke Osborne (11)
Querns School

BE AFRAID

Be afraid,
I'm coming for you
I'll come through the window
Or come from the loo.

I will come at you at the dead of night
And you'll scream and scream with terrible
Fright.
You won't see me, but you'll know I'm there
Because I'll make noises that will give you
A scare!

So be afraid I'm coming, you'll see
With a brush of your hair
Or the cold feel of me.

Hugh Rochfort (10)
Querns School

SPACE WORLD

See the space in the night,
It might give you a fright.
See little Mars on his own,
Pluto comes and asks for his bone.
Jupiter says 'Hello Venus again,
Let's go and dance out and about.'
Sun and Moon heard a shout,
So they were screaming about.
The Earth and the little Smurf,
So goodbye to all planets.

Jade Sperrin (9)
St Anne's CE Primary School

THE DOLPHIN RACE

A dolphin argument began to sail,
Over the seven seas,
Between two dolphins called Jack and Jade,
One went red like cherries.

The argument started when Jack told Jade,
He was faster then her,
Other dolphins started to crowd around,
The crowd began to stir.

A decision was made to have a race,
Around the island and back,
Jack said, 'OK, I'll beat her any time,'
Jade said 'Losers sleep in sacks!'

So, the race began, very nail biting,
Suddenly, someone saw Jade,
Whizzing ahead of the big-headed Jack,
So the decision was made.

When Jack got back he decided to apologise,
Because of his rude comments,
So, the story goes on to tell how
Jack and Jade became friends.

Joanne Gray (10)
St Anne's CE Primary School

I HATE GOING SHOPPING

I hate going shopping, it makes me
really mad, Mum can't stand it either
I should have stayed with Dad.

Up and down the aisle with a trolley
full of food, people pushing and shoving
I'm getting in the mood.

We're going through the checkout
I'm nearly home and dry
I can see the door, I think
I'm going to cry!

Hayley Entwistle (9)
St Anne's CE Primary School

WHAT AM I?

I'm slippery and slimy,
I would love to be your best friend
I know we would be in the end.

Splish, splash in the water,
I think that I am quite graceful
I really think I am quite spaceful.
Do you know what I am yet?

I am quite fat and long,
I use my fins to slide on.
In a second of swimming I am gone.

I am usually grey,
I love to play.
And my size is usually 5 ton!

Have you guessed yet?
I am a *sealion!*

Laura Exton (10)
St Anne's CE Primary School

WHAT AM I?

I'm brown, grey and black,
I crawl up your back.
I'm very hairy,
I'm very scary,
What am I?

I have eight legs,
I love your eggs,
I have lots of eyes,
I sleep in Dad's ties.
What am I?

My body's crispy,
My sister's wispy,
I'm not very big,
I am not a pig.
What am I?

I make silk,
I drink milk,
My friend is called Deb,
She lives on a web,
I'm a spider!

Emma Davies (9)
St Anne's CE Primary School

WHAT WILL HAPPEN IN THE NEXT 2000 YEARS

What will happen? Will cat's talk?
I'm sure teddy's will do your homework!
I hope my dog can read stories to people,
There will be a robot to cook meals!

Pigs will fly in the clouds,
There will be a big bird for a plane,
There will be no gravity,
You could walk on the ceiling,
That's what I think,
Will happen in the next 2000 years.

Amie Strawford (9)
St Anne's CE Primary School

WHAT AM I?

I'm hot and big
And shine away
Getting hotter every day.

I'm hot and round
I am bigger
Than ground and
Every day I shine away.

I'm the biggest star
Ever made
I keep Earth warm
Anyway I begin with S and
End with N.

Answer: I am the sun.

Tom Worlock (9)
St Anne's CE Primary School

WHO AM I?

I cause computer disruption
And major destruction
People are puzzled
Of all the machines I've nuzzled.

Computers are worried
People are sorry
They didn't see
It really is me.

I really exist
I give your hard drive the fist.

Who am I?

Adam Costello (9)
St Anne's CE Primary School

BIRDY, BIRDY

Birdy, birdy flying high,
In the crystal clear blue sky.

Birdy, birdy there's a hawk,
Watch out birdy, you're being stalked.

Birdy, birdy death is near,
Birdy, birdy is filled with fear.

Birdy, birdy there's a gun,
Birdy, birdy has been done.

Tamasyn Russell (10)
St Anne's CE Primary School

SCHOOL DINNER DISASTERS

Lumpy mash, mushy peas,
Edward dropped his dinner on his knees.

Cold custard ran down his back,
The dinner ladies got the sack.

They hired a dinner lady called Betty,
She served up burnt baked beans and spaghetti.

The spaghetti was yuck, the beans were worse,
I think they must have been cursed.

Is this really how we should be fed,
This is a school dinner disaster.

Louise Fenner (9)
St Anne's CE Primary School

A 2000 STAR

Star of silver burning bright,
Floating across the lonely night,
Shine and make the night go light,
It's 2000 so don't go away,
The year 2000 is a very special time,
We need you to brighten up the sky,
In 2000 without you we won't have anything to do,
The first time I saw you I thought it was magic,
Now I have to say goodbye to
A 2000 star.

Emily Meddings (9)
St Anne's CE Primary School

WHO AM I?

I am smaller than the rest,
People think I'm the best,
I have the same name as a dog,
No one can see me in the fog.

I'm thin not fat,
I am like a ball,
I am very small
And no one can see me.

I am the furthest from the sun,
I am opposite than another one.

Answer is Pluto.

Joshua Farmer (9)
St Anne's CE Primary School

LITTER BUG

Bad litter bugs,
I hate you all,
All around the street you are.

Evil bug, nasty bug,
Horrible bug, you are.
You are destroying countryside.

Destroying towns and cities,
You are a disease,
To the world.

Danny Fosh (9)
St Anne's CE Primary School

EVERYTHING'S MISSING

I can't find my clothes,
I can't find my bag,
I can't find my shoes,
I can't find my lunch-box,
I can't find my toothbrush,
I can't find the stairs,
Oh, I've found my bed!

Hannah Joy (9)
St Anne's CE Primary School

BUBBLEGUM!

Chewing gum,
Sticky gum,
I prefer bubblegum.
Look at this bubble,
Oh I'll get into trouble,
Let's get out of here.
I'll blow a bubble as I run at a pace,
I'll make it pop all over my face.
The gum that makes me blow a bubble,
Always gets me into trouble,
Bubblegum,
Sticky gum,
I think I prefer chewing gum!

Timothy Marston (11)
St Lawrence CE Primary School, Lechlade

ELEPHANT

She moves slow, she moves fast
She moves the world.
Down, down thuds her feet on the dust, dirt
Swish, swash goes her tail in the hot safari sun.
Up and around goes her long curly nose
Spraying cool fans of water on her rough, dirty body
And then on her young, too small to do it themselves.
Then there's her soft, long call to the rest of the herd,
Saying we must move on to the sweet, green leaves of the safari trees
But I must warn you of her stride and
That her calls ring out nation-wide.

Sally Ann Mayo (11)
St Lawrence CE Primary School, Lechlade

MY LITTLE BROTHER

I had a little brother
No bigger than my thumb.

I put him in the coffee pot
He rattled like a drum.

I made him a little bath
I soaked him until he was crinkled.

I put him in his bed
He squeaked like a pimple.

Laura Woolley (11)
St Lawrence CE Primary School, Lechlade

BEWARE OF BILLY JEW

I'm the boss of this playground
My name is Billy Jew
I like to beat up children
And tell them what to do.

If someone's happy, when I'm around
I'll go over there and give them a pound,
(I don't mean money)

I'm the boss of this playground,
My name is Billy Jew.
I like to beat up children
And tell them what to do.

Someone tried to stand up to me,
But I put them straight,
I lifted and threw them at the gate
(What a hit too)

I'm the boss of this playground
My name is Billy Jew.
I like to beat up children
And tell them what to do.

So beware of Billy Jew.

Heather Brookes (11)
St Lawrence CE Primary School, Lechlade

THE SLITHERY SNAKE

The slithery snake slides through the jungle
Sticking out his long, long toungle.
Swallows his food like he's really hungle
and sleeps in his special jungle bungle.

Lorna White (10)
St Lawrence CE Primary School, Lechlade

DOLPHIN

Splish, splash, here we go
On our way to Mexico
Splosh, splish up, up high
I think I could touch the sky
Sometimes we get caught in the net
And even sometimes kept as pets
Don't put in that horrible potion
Because it's such a lovely ocean
I hate all those nasty sharks
But they can't even play on parks
I'm a dolphin, 1, 2, 3
Jumping and diving, look at me.

Howard Read (11)
St Lawrence CE Primary School, Lechlade

THE LION'S PLAN

You can't see me, but here I am.
I'm out here hunting and this is my plan.
I'm going to pounce when they come near,
When they all come over here.
When they see me they will run,
And that will be when I come.
I'll run and run and run and run
Until I slash one with my claw
I will eat and eat and eat some more.

Luke Keegan (10)
St Lawrence CE Primary School, Lechlade

WHO LOVES CRICKET

Cricket is the game with the bat and ball,
and I think people are mad that don't like it at all.
With the umpire shouting four or maybe six,
and the batsman doing his little tricks.
For in February the cricket season will start again,
with players playing for England that started practising since
                                        they were nine or ten.
There's Husain, Gough, Atherton and Stuart,
if you practise the game then I'm sure you can do it.
For one day I wish that for England I will play,
when I'm out on the cricket square on a beautiful summer's day.

Sam Greenhalgh (10)
St Lawrence CE Primary School, Lechlade

A HORSE'S DAY

Clip, clop, clip, clop
says the horses as they trot
out in the wind and the rain
can't wait to be home again.
Nice warm stable
all rugged up, fresh hay
boy, what a day.

Jessica Paterson (10)
St Lawrence CE Primary School, Lechlade

BILL

I know a boy called Bill
who lives up a hill.
He likes playing ball,
but he's no good at all.
He should stop acting the fool
and go back to school.

Phillip Curtis (10)
St Lawrence CE Primary School, Lechlade

FOOTBALL CRAZY

Muddy pitch.
Thumbs itch.
Crucial match.
Slippery patch.
Hits his head.
Back to bed.
Reduced to ten.
Name was Ben.
Round of applause.
Owen scores.
Need of food.
In a bad mood.
What a bad score.
I'm afraid there's no more!

Sam Clegg (9)
Tuffley Primary School

FA CUP

Newcastle.	No hassle.
Man U.	Crowds boo.
Goal keepers.	Stadium sweepers.
Keane off.	That's tough.
Sheringham on.	Goal keeper gone.
HE scores.	Loud applause.
One - nil.	Shouts Bill.
Alan Shearer.	Gets nearer.
He's glad.	His dad.
Turns up.	For the cup.
Paul Scholes.	Second goal.
End of game.	Winning team's name

Man U.

Shaun Beresford (9)
Tuffley Primary School

KENNING

A noise-maker,
A toy-maker,
A bad-stinker,
A paper-lover,
A smack-hater,
A mess-maker,
A food-thrower,
A heavy-sleeper.
What am I?
A baby.

Jade Innes (10)
Tuffley Primary School

SEASONS

Summer is the time,
When we wear bright colours,
It's always hot,
I like all summers.

Autumn is the time,
When I can fly my kite,
Although it's a little cold,
Still coldness doesn't bite.

Winter is the time,
When the temperature drops,
Christmas is coming,
So everyone shops.

Spring is the time,
When daffodils grow,
It's rainy and sunny,
To form a rainbow.

Jade Ryan (10)
Tuffley Primary School

CAMP WEATHER

Weather damp,
Horrible camp.
Long pikes,
No one likes.
Horrible bites,
From biting mites.

Teacher snoring,
How boring!
Muscles aching,
Dawn breaking,
Long nights,
I might
Just sleep!

Paula Thomas (9)
Tuffley Primary School

A KENNING POEM

A smooth-shiner,
A sweet-taster,
A light-green,
A mother-tree,
An easy-bruiser,
A rosy-red,
A water-drinker,
A maggot-hater.

An apple.

Stella Davis (10)
Tuffley Primary School

WHAT AM I?

A football player
A mud lover
A lovely dinner
A revolting smell
A food grabber
A noise maker
A heavy weighter
A slow runner.

A brother.

Louis Preece (11)
Tuffley Primary School

THE HORSE POEM

A horse trots
Clippety clop
Trots every day
Own special way
Lovely pace
Bright face
Swishing tail
Like a whale.

Rachel Johnson (10)
Tuffley Primary School

SNAKES

Snakes aren't scary
Because they're not hairy
Snakes aren't mean
They're always clean
Snakes aren't horrible
They're adorable
Snakes aren't small
They're cool!
But . . .
Snakes can be
Killers!

Danny Hammond (10)
Tuffley Primary School